101
Brain Boosters

Terry Eckmann, Ph.D.

ISBN: 978-1-60679-273-5
Library of Congress Control Number: 2013938432
Cover design: Cheery Sugabo
Book layout: Bean Creek Studio
Front cover photo: Comstock Images

Healthy Learning
P.O. Box 1828
Monterey, CA 93942
www.healthylearning.com

Dedication

This book is dedicated to my family. Thanks to my children, Cole and Katie, and to my husband, Bock, for your love and support always. Thanks to my mom and dad, Cliff and Marion Ferebee; you have forever encouraged and supported me in every personal and professional endeavor. You are amazing. Garnet Cox, you have inspired me since my college years, you are the best adopted mom ever! Iris and Wally Eckmann, thanks for being dream in-laws! You have been a special bonus in my marriage to your son.

It is my hope that this book serves as a resource for all lifelong learners who embrace a brain-healthy lifestyle. May you live longer and better.

Acknowledgments

Writing a book that embraces my passion for lifelong learning and a healthy brain and body has been on my bucket list for years. Thanks to Jim Peterson, who encouraged me to make that goal a priority with my first book, *101 Brain Boosters*. Dr. John Torgerson and Dr. David Williams were two of my favorite Minot State University professors in my undergraduate and graduate studies in speech-language pathology. They helped to fuel my fascination with the brain and how it works. I enjoyed working as a speech therapist and satisfied my love for exercise and music by teaching "aerobics" after my "day" job ended each day at 4:00. I opened Body By Choice Exercise Studio and found myself with two full-time jobs! Well, three, if you count the hours I spent mixing music from my "albums" to "cassettes." Thank you Peter and Kathie Davis for the International Dance-Exercise Association, now IDEA Health & Fitness Association. Your vision truly made a difference for all of us who began our professional fitness journeys in the 1980s. You have truly inspired the world to fitness.

I went on to earn a second graduate degree in physical education with an emphasis in health and fitness program development and exercise science. This degree required a capstone project and gave me the opportunity to explore another passion, working with older adults. I approached Arlo Pretzer at Trinity Hospital with my idea of doing research on the effects of exercise on the health and fitness of older adults. Thank you Arlo for believing in me and thank you to all of the "recycled teenagers" who traveled the world with me to model what good health and fitness looks like. That first research project turned into a 12-year full-time job with the hospital—and then another door opened.

Thanks to Dr. David Rochholz for that phone call: "Terry, there is a job at Minot State University that would be a good fit for you." I have loved every job I have had but the past 14 years at Minot State University has been the icing on the cake. I furthered my education with a Ph.D. in educational leadership and embraced the opportunity to research emotional intelligence in the fitness industry, as well as my number one passion: how does exercise impact the brain and body in the aging process? Thanks to Dr. Deb Jensen for the Learning & the Brain® Conference that introduced me to Dr. John Ratey, Dr. Gary Small, and Dr. Paul Nussbaum and their incredible research supporting exercise as a critical domain of a brain-healthy lifestyle. It was a boost in my interest to further study and research exercise and brain health. I have been blessed to have a career that embraces my many passions.

Thanks to Pat Jorgenson for all your time and expertise during our walks this summer as this book came together. Your experience as a teacher and support as a friend is appreciated. Thanks to Beth Helfrich for "boosting" the title. Thanking everyone who has impacted my life would be another book. I appreciate each and every person who has touched my life.

And last, but certainly not least, thanks to you for including *101 Brain Boosters* in your library of lifelong learning. Again, it is my hope that this book serves as a resource for all lifelong learners who embrace a brain-healthy lifestyle. May you live longer and better.

Contents

1. Sit less, and move more. Sitting deactivates the brain, moving activates the brain.

2. Exercise! Exercise improves brain health and stimulates brain growth.

3. Engage in aerobic exercise like jogging, running, and biking to stimulate brain-derived neurotrophic factor (BDNF), which neuroscientists consider fertilizer for the brain.

4. Walk to increase cognitive functioning and brain volume.

5. Dance to reduce risk of Alzheimer's by up to 65 percent.

6. Get active with Zumba® Fitness to engage in four critical domains of a brain-healthy lifestyle.

7. Swim to increase blood flow to the brain in a non-impact way.

8. Strength train to improve the brain's executive functioning.

9. Add interval training to your exercise program to boost metabolism and maintain a healthy weight.

10. Stretch to increase cerebrospinal fluid flow to crucial areas of the brain.

11. Practice yoga to improve mood and decrease anxiety.

12. Do Pilates to enhance coordination of the mind, body, and spirit.

13. Try Tai Chi to put meditation in motion while learning invigorating motor sequences.

14. Develop the core to guard the body and brain against falls and to improve posture.

15. Get involved in group exercise to music because it reduces your sense of fatigue so that you are able to work harder and longer.

16. Play sports as a way to connect with others and challenge your cerebellum with complex movement patterns.

17. Perform balance activities that will strengthen the vestibular system and connect the visual, spatial, and motor areas of the brain.

18. Take the stairs as a way to add fitness into your life while energizing your brain and strengthening your lower body.

19. Plant a garden to lower levels of the stress hormone cortisol while improving mood and burning up to 300 calories an hour.

20. Improve brain efficiency with exercise.

21. Play Wii™ sports and fitness games with friends and family to increase movement and activate brains during social gatherings.

22. Move your joints through a full range of motion to stimulate fluids that strengthen neuromuscular connections, thereby facilitating safe and fluid body movement.

23. Sit in good posture to send a signal of strength and confidence to the brain and to optimize space for organs in the abdominal area to work efficiently.

24. Energize with Brain Gym® movements that activate the brain for optimal storage and retrieval of information.

25. Manage stress effectively to decrease levels of stress hormones, increase blood flow to the brain, decrease anxiety and depression, boost memory, and optimize brain functioning.

26. Be aware of emotional, behavioral, physical, and cognitive stress symptoms (or signals) so you know when chronic stress is hurting your body and brain.

27. Think positively. Negative thinking releases toxic hormones in your body that will make your brain and your body unhealthy.

28. Use progressive relaxation to lower levels of stress hormones (like cortisol) in the body and to train the body to control the fight-or-flight response.

29. Practice breathing exercises to expand lung volume and increase blood flow to the brain, because the brain uses 20 percent of the body's oxygen.

30. Minimize the stress in your life by not overcommitting.

31. Get adequate sleep to give the brain the time it needs to regenerate neurons and build memories.

32. Take a nap to recharge your brain.

33. Get a massage to increase mood-enhancing chemicals like serotonin and dopamine and lower the stress hormone cortisol.

34. Disconnect from technology to allow the brain down time to go over experiences, solidify information, and convert information to long-term memory.

35. Talk to someone to disengage from negative thinking or worry.

36. Listen to music to improve mood, lower the stress response, boost the immune system, enhance exercising, fight fatigue, and increase productivity.

37. Laugh to boost the immune system, reduce muscle tension, and release endorphins, the "feel-good hormones" in your brain.

38. Enjoy nature. Natural surroundings allow the brain to renew and replenish.

39. Eat a healthy diet for a healthy brain. What and how you eat is crucial to brain health.

40. Chew more, and eat less. It takes the brain up to 20 minutes to register that the stomach is full. Healthy weight = healthy brain and body.

41. Drink water (approximately 80 percent of the brain is water). Dehydration leads to limited ability to concentrate and make decisions.

42. Fuel your brain with a healthy breakfast to provide the glucose it needs for optimal functioning as you begin your day.

43. Maintain a healthy weight. People who are obese have twice the risk of developing dementia.

44. Watch portion sizes and avoid supersizing to avoid unnecessary weight gain. Eating too much in one meal reduces oxygen flow to the brain.

45. Eat fruits and vegetables to reduce risk of cognitive impairment by reducing oxidative stress to the brain.

46. Prevent low and high blood sugar for the brain to function at optimal level.

47. Consume omega-3 fatty acids, which are key in transmitting information in the brain.

48. Stimulate the brain with a variety of mental activities for better brain health across the lifespan.

49. Travel to introduce your brain to new places and different ways to get there to increase synaptogenesis (growth of connections between neurons).

50. Play sudoku to challenge the left hemisphere of the brain to find number patterns. Do crossword puzzles to challenge the language and memory areas of the brain.

51. Be aware of the effects of lighting and color on the brain.

52. Read a book, magazine, or newspaper to establish new connections in your brain.

53. Join a book club to challenge your brain to absorb the perspectives of others on things you read.

54. Pay attention to key numbers for better health.

55. Develop new talents. Knit, paint, or learn a new sport to challenge your brain and body to work together in new ways.

56. Learn a new word or fact each day to enhance your brain's ability to make new memories.

57. Take a different route to a usual destination to take your brain off autopilot; new directions make new connections.

58. Play board, card, or computer games with friends and on your own to improve your ability to concentrate, while boosting neuronal growth with new activities.

59. Socialize to decrease loneliness, depression, and stress while boosting brain connections. Socialization is a critical domain of a brain-healthy lifestyle.

60. Volunteer to connect with others, boost self-confidence, and increase life satisfaction.

61. Join clubs and recreational groups to develop new friendships, learn different things, stay active, and keep the brain engaged.

62. Attend a conference. It is a great way to strengthen what you know and learn new things while developing new relationships.

63. Learn a second language.

64. Ask questions and listen; practice Stephen Covey's "Seek first to understand, then to be understood" to achieve empathetic listening and boost memory.

65. Exercise with a friend. It will keep you accountable for your exercise plans and give you something to look forward to doing.

66. Keep a "grateful journal" by writing down at least one good thing that happened in your day, which helps to train your brain to make positive memories.

67. Meditate to make stronger connections between brain regions and experience less brain atrophy.

68. Think about what you are thinking to take control of your thoughts, enhance cognitive flexibility, and strengthen your ability to know and govern yourself.

69. Practice mindfulness by focusing on what is happening around you without judgment to reduce stress, depression, and anxiety.

70. Use your nondominant side more often to create pathways across your left- and right-brain hemispheres.

71. Take brain breaks because a person's attention span is 8 to 20 minutes, depending on age and interest in the subject matter.

72. Engage in chair marching to move the large muscles of your body to increase blood and oxygen flow to the brain.

73. Perform seated or standing cross-lateral movement to strengthen the corpus callosum, the part of the brain that connects right and left hemispheres.

74. Energize with chair dancing to a wide variety of music, and stimulate your brain and body to move to varied rhythm patterns.

75. Give the brain time to process and learn.

76. Eat from the four food groups.

77. Stand up and sit down to fit fitness into your life and energize your brain while doing one of the top five exercises for lower body: a squat.

78. Whirl and twirl and spin and turn around to stimulate alertness and attention, and to improve reading skills.

79. Sit on a stability ball to improve focus and ability to stay on task; engaging the body engages the brain.

80. Do a walking review on your own or with someone; say things you are learning out loud while moving, so that the brain is getting oxygen-rich blood while rehearsing.

81. Go outside and get sunshine and fresh air to reduce depression, regulate melatonin (the sleep hormone), and lower levels of cortisol (the stress hormone).

82. Be a lifelong learner to keep your brain active and growing.

83. Pay attention. The intention to focus leads to retention of information.

84. Engage in rehearsal/overlearn because information remains in short-term memory for only 15 to 20 seconds unless you anchor the learning in meaningful ways.

85. Develop the three memory pathways—semantic (meaning), episodic (stories), and procedural (how to)—in order to retain and retrieve memory.

86. Use all learning modalities. Link visual, auditory, and kinesthetic activity in the learning process to strengthen connections in the brain.

87. Tap into multiple intelligences to engage a variety of learning styles; learn through your strengths to improve your weaknesses.

88. Engage emotions like joy, enthusiasm, and awe to facilitate learning; emotions trigger chemicals that signal the brain "this is important, so keep it."

89. Reduce learned helplessness by taking control of choices; make a decision to believe you can achieve goals and deal with life challenges in a positive manner.

90. Use mnemonics as a way to organize and remember information.

91. Utilize novelty in learning because the brain is attracted to new and fun things; learning happens with novelty.

92. Promote quality physical education because exercise helps prepare the brain for optimal learning; children who exercise do better in school.

93. Make connections. Knowledge derives from connections; the essence of memory is linking one thought to another.

94. Protect your brain. Guard your brain to avoid injury.

95. Strengthen your senses to engage more of your brain; the brain learns best when more of the five senses are involved.

96. Develop spatial abilities to stimulate growth of neurons and dendrites in the part of the brain where spatial abilities reside, typically in the hippocampus and the parietal lobe.

97. Play a musical instrument to enhance the ability to process and remember auditory information.

98. Believe in yourself. If you think you can or think you can't, you are right.

99. Don't smoke. It robs the brain of oxygen.

100. Drink alcohol moderately or not at all. Alcohol damages brain cells and interferes with communication between brain cells. Don't do drugs.

101. Don't just know it; *do it.* What you do with what you know is the key to making a difference in your brain and your life.

Introduction

101 Brain Boosters provides key practices that are conducive to a healthy brain and productive lifelong learning. Average life expectancy is approximately 78.7 years. Research indicates that longevity is based on two major factors: genetics and lifestyle choices. People are living longer and want to live better. *101 Brain Boosters* provides 101 tips to keep the brain healthy, happy, and productive. *101 Brain Boosters* includes research-based, brain-healthy choices from the following critical domains: exercise, nutrition, stress management, mental stimulation, socialization, and spirituality. Also included are key strategies to enhance learning throughout the lifespan. This book offers readers 101 ways to achieve optimal brain functioning at all ages and stages of life.

#1: Sit less, and move more. Sitting deactivates the brain, moving activates the brain.

When a person sits for more than 20 minutes, it becomes increasingly more difficult to pay attention, and it is common to fall asleep. When a person sits, blood pools in the legs and doesn't deliver the oxygen and glucose the brain needs to do its work. The brain needs oxygen and glucose to stay alert. The brain uses 20 percent of the brain's oxygen and glucose.

Research as early as the 1950s showed that men in physically active jobs had less coronary artery disease. Recent research suggests a strong association between long periods of sitting and mortality risk from all causes, including cardiovascular disease. Sitting increases girth measurements and lowers body metabolism. Sitting also deactivates the brain.

It is estimated that approximately 70 to 80 percent of the waking day is spent sitting, which is a lot of time for the brain (and body) to be inactive. Sitting time includes riding in a car, eating a meal at a table, playing video games, working at a computer, watching television, or reading in a seated position. The traditional school and office environments are not designed with the brain (or body) in mind. The brain is least productive when sitting; yet, people are seated when doing most of their work. Sitting on a stability ball in place of a chair would activate the body and the brain to increase productivity. Standing desk stations are another option to be considered. It would be ideal to have desktops on stationary bikes or treadmills in schools and workplaces. Following are a few ideas for you to implement to sit less and move more:

- Stand up and sit down (as many times as you can).
- Take a 60-second walk.
- Read in a yoga V-sit position.
- Do 10 jumping jacks after 10 to 20 minutes of sitting.
- Perform 10 or more crunches (sit-ups).
- Walk up and down stairs for 60 seconds.
- Move into a proud warrior pose.
- Do push-ups off the wall, a desk, or a table.
- Complete a chore, such as watering a plant, unloading the dishwasher, or cleaning out a desk.
- Get up, and get a drink of water.
- Stand up and stretch.
- Get up and dance.
- Check out brain boosters #70 through #80 for more energizer activities.

#2: Exercise! Exercise improves brain health and stimulates brain growth.

Exercise is one of the best ways to counter the process of aging on the brain. Without exercise, the heart, lungs, and muscles work less efficiently together, so the brain gets less of the blood, oxygen, and glucose necessary for optimal functioning. Inactivity begins to affect brain volume between the ages of 30 and 40, decreasing approximately 5 percent per decade of life because of the limited blood flow and subsequent loss of neurons and dendrites in the brain. Lack of physical activity is also a risk factor for heart disease, diabetes, cancer, stroke, obesity, and high blood pressure. These conditions also have an effect on health.

Regular exercise increases brain health and growth. Blood flow to the brain is increased when exercising. This upsurge in blood flow increases the number and size of the capillaries in the brain. Exercise also promotes neurogenesis, the growth of neurons, in the brain. Neuronal dendrites increase in number and size with regular exercise. The increases in blood volume, growth and development of capillaries, and neuronal and dendritic growth all play a role in making the brain bigger and healthier.

ACSM Recommendations for Exercise for a Healthy Adult

Cardiovascular Exercise

- Participate in 150 minutes of moderate-intensity exercise per week.
- Strive for 30 to 60 minutes of moderate-intensity exercise (five days per week) or 20 to 60 minutes of vigorous-intensity exercise (three days per week).
- One continuous session and multiple shorter sessions (of at least 10 minutes) is preferred.
- Gradual progression of exercise time, frequency, and intensity helps adherence.
- People unable to meet these minimums can still benefit from some activity.

Resistance Exercise

- Train each major muscle group two or three days each week.
- Use a variety of exercises and equipment.
- Very light or light intensity is best for older persons or previously sedentary adults starting exercise.
- Adults should wait at least 48 hours between resistance training sessions.

Flexibility Exercise

- Do flexibility exercises at least two or three days each week
- Each stretch should be held 10 to 30 seconds at the point of tightness or slight discomfort.
- Flexibility exercise is most effective when the muscle is warm. Try light aerobic activity or a hot bath to warm the muscles before stretching.

Resources for more information on exercise recommendations can be found at www.acsm.org.

Exercise is medicine. What is good for the body is good for the brain. The next 22 brain boosters will provide insight into how a variety of exercises can make a difference in your brain health.

iStockphoto/Thinkstock

#3: Engage in aerobic exercise like jogging, running, and biking to stimulate brain-derived neurotrophic factor (BDNF), which neuroscientists consider fertilizer for the brain.

Jogging, running, and biking are three common and popular aerobic activities. The term *aerobics* was coined by Dr. Kenneth Cooper. *Aerobic* means "with oxygen." Exercise is considered aerobic when you are working in your training heart rate zone. The Karvonen formula is a mathematical formula that helps determine your training heart rate zone. A person needs to use age and resting heart rate to determine training heart rate zone. Following is an example for an individual 30 years of age with a resting heart rate of 65:

- Step 1: 220 – 30 (age) = 190 (max heart rate)
- Step 2: 190 (max heart rate) – 65 (resting heart rate) = 125 (max heart rate reserve)
- Step 3: 125 (max heart rate reserve) x .50 = 62.5 (low end of heart rate zone)

  and

  125 (max heart rate reserve) x .85 = 106.25 (high end of heart rate zone)
- Step 4: 62.5 (low end of heart rate zone) + 65 (resting heart rate) = 127.5

  and

  106.25 (high end of heart rate zone) + 65 (resting heart rate) = 171.25

The target heart rate zone for this person would be 127 to 171 beats per minute.

It is best to measure heart rate during exercise at the radial artery, placing your pointer and middle finger of your right hand on the radial artery on your left wrist just below your thumb line or your carotid artery (place your fingers at the top of your neck, just under your jaw at about the mid-point between your earlobe and chin). Make sure to keep moving as you check your heart rate. Once you know how your body feels when you are in your training heart rate zone you can use rate of perceived exertion (RPE). The simplest method is to identify how hard you are working on a scale of 1 to 10. You should be working between a 5 and 8 on a scale of 1 to 10.

Biking, jogging, and running are three aerobic activities that will stimulate brain-derived neurotrophic factor (BDNF). BDNF has been the focus of a great deal of research in the past 20 years. Neuroscientists discovered that BDNF is released in the body and brain when people do aerobic exercise. BDNF nourishes neurons like fertilizer, stimulating growth of neurons (neurogenesis) and growth of dendritic branches. A neuron is like a tree with branches (the dendrites) and leaves (the secondary dendrites). BDNF helps to grow more dendrites (branches) and secondary dendrites (leaves) to create more connections. BDNF improves the functions of neurons in many ways: encouraging neuronal growth, strengthening and protecting against cell death, and activating connections between neurons to strengthen communication in the brain. BDNF does a great deal of its work in the hippocampus of the brain (area related to memory and learning).

Adults should get at least 150 minutes of moderate-intensity exercise per week. Aerobic exercise is key in boosting brain health and memory. Biking, jogging, and running are three good options to engage in aerobic exercise. The key is to find aerobic exercise that you enjoy to take advantage of the body and brain benefits associated with working in your training heart rate zone.

iStockphoto/Thinkstock

#4: Walk to increase cognitive functioning and brain volume.

Walking is man's best medicine.

—Hippocrates

For centuries, walking has been considered one of the most beneficial forms of exercise. John Medina, in his book *Brain Rules*, suggests that the human body was designed to walk 12 miles a day.

Walking is good for the body and the brain. One study found that women who walked at an easy pace at least 1.5 hours a week had better cognitive function and less cognitive decline than women who walked less than 40 minutes per week. Walking at a brisk pace in your training heart rate zone can also build brain volume by increasing blood flow to the brain, which in turn increases capillary density in the brain. Walking also stimulates an increase in neurons and growth of dendrites, especially in the hippocampus of the brain, which adds to brain growth. People who walked between 6 and 9 miles per week had more gray matter volume 9 years after the start of a study than those who didn't walk as much. Researchers suggest that those who walk the most cut their risk of developing memory loss by almost half.

Walking has long been the most popular form of exercise in the United States. The following are tips to maximize safety and effectiveness of a walking program:

- Walk at a brisk pace, try to stay within training heart rate zone (see #4).
- Invest in a good pair of walking shoes. It is an investment; pay now for a good pair of shoes, or pay later with an injury. Wear those shoes only when you walk for exercise. Your body will tell you when it is time for a new pair of shoes with sore ankles or knees or possibly low back pain. A good pair of walking shoes may last 6 to 9 months.
- Wear a pedometer to chart your steps. It is a good way to reinforce exercise and to chart progress.
- Choose a variety of walking trails to keep walks interesting and different.
- Walk hills to challenge your cardiovascular system.
- Vary the pace of the walk to challenge the body, walk at a medium pace for 5 minutes and at a quick pace for a minute. Gradually increase quicker intervals to burn more calories and get more oxygen to the brain.
- Walk to music to set your pace. Choose music that is 128 beats per minute up to 140+ beats per minute will work for most walkers. Create a personalized music mix or purchase music from companies like Powermix Music or Dynamix Music. The music for step or low-medium impact aerobics will usually work to set the pace for walking.

- Start slowly, and gradually increase time or length and speed of the walk.
- Log the walking workouts to reinforce and celebrate the time invested in walking for your brain and body.

#5: Dance to reduce risk of Alzheimer's by up to 65 percent.

Numerous studies support that dancing reduces the risk of dementia and Alzheimer's by up to 65 percent. Dancing can improve aerobic power, lower body muscle endurance, strength and flexibility. The balance and agility gained through dance can prevent falls, which plays a role in brain safety. Dancing also conditions the brain to better regulate stress and gain a sense of control over self.

Taking a dance class with a partner to learn social dances like the waltz, tango, salsa, merengue, cha-cha, and swing is a good place to begin. Learning to perform movement patterns to the beat of music challenges the hippocampus, cerebellum, frontal lobe, prefrontal cortex, motor cortex, parietal lobe, occipital lobe, and temporal lobe to work together to learn movement and process rhythm. The frontal lobe (the library of the brain) where information is held and the prefrontal cortex (the conductor and decision maker of the brain), along with the motor cortex and cerebellum work together in dance to help the brain and body work together to send appropriate messages through the motor neurons for everything from hand and foot placement, to moving around in the space of a room. The temporal and parietal lobes process the sound of the music to move to the beat of the music. The occipital lobe processes the visual modeling by the instructor and scans the dancing space to move safely around the room.

Line dancing was especially popular in the 1990s. Line dancing provides a great opportunity to get on the dance floor without a partner or to get a group of people moving together on the dance floor. There are many options for learning line and partner dances. A dance class is ideal. Christy Lane is an excellent dance teacher and has instructional dance DVDs and music available on www.christylane.com. There are dances for all ages and stages of life to get you moving to the beat of music. Dancing at home in the living room, kitchen, or any room with enough space is a convenient option.

Dance is also a great option to get aerobic exercise, which provides brain benefits like elevation of BDNF to stimulate neurogenesis (especially in the hippocampus), increase in neurotransmitters that improve mood and focus (dopamine, serotonin, and norepinephrine), and upsurge in levels of VEGF (vascular endothelial growth factor) to strengthen and grow capillaries in the brain. All of these molecules boost brain health and growth to prevent dementia and Alzheimer's. The social interaction of dance can be an added bonus.

#6: Get active with Zumba Fitness to engage in four critical domains of a brain-healthy lifestyle.

Four of the critical domains of a brain-healthy lifestyle are physical activity, socialization, mental stimulation, and stress management. Zumba Fitness engages all four. Zumba Fitness provides rich and challenging movement along with intellectual stimulation creating an environment that has positive lifelong consequences for the brain.

Zumba Fitness is effective *aerobic exercise* that strengthens the cardiovascular system. Zumba Fitness also incorporates a significant amount of cross-lateral movement (arm and/or leg crossing the midline of the body), which strengthens the corpus callosum, creating stronger connections between the right and left brain hemispheres.

Zumba Fitness creates a *social environment* with energizing Latin dance music and moves. The Zumba program currently offers eight types of Zumba classes designed for individuals throughout the lifespan. The Zumba Fitness concept is to create a Zumba Fitness-Party led by trained and licensed Zumba instructors. The Zumba program facilitates friendships in and out of classes and within the ZIN network.

Zumba Fitness challenges the brain with a progressive sequence of moves in a noncompetitive atmosphere to provide *mental stimulation*. Zumba exercise pairs the known with novel movement in a nonthreatening way to enhance learning and build muscle memory.

Zumba Fitness dance and party atmosphere is an invigorating and healthy way to *effectively manage stress*. The party atmosphere stimulates a feeling of happiness. The Latin dance movement gets the heart pumping and the blood flowing while lowering levels of the stress hormone cortisol and balancing hormones and neurotransmitters like serotonin, dopamine, and norepinephrine to help the brain and body stay in balance.

#7: Swim to increase blood flow to the brain in a non-impact way.

Swimming is an excellent form of aerobic exercise and the lack of ground impact protects joints from stress and strain. Swimming improves the ability of the body to take in, transport, and use oxygen. When your body transports and uses oxygen efficiently, blood flow to the brain improves as well.

Weight-bearing exercises like walking, jogging, and running are excellent aerobic activities. Adding swimming as a way to cross-train with a non-impact activity gives the joints a break while challenging muscles in a different way. The intensity of your swim will determine how many calories you burn and how much blood is flowing through your brain and body. Push yourself to work in your training heart rate zone (50 to 85 percent) or use the rate of perceived exertion of 1 to 10 (work between 5 and 8).

Shallow and deep vertical water exercise are good non- to low-impact ways to get a safe and effective workout. The buoyant force of the water results in about a 90 percent reduction of body weight while in the water. The density of water is 800 times the density of air, so the water provides full body resistance and is also a good form of training for muscle strength and endurance. Water exercise provides a way to burn calories and increase blood flow to the brain with little strain to the body.

George Doyle

#8: Strength train to improve the brain's executive functioning.

Cognition refers to the mental action or process of acquiring knowledge and understanding through thought, experience, and the senses. The mental processes considered cognition include attention, memory, producing and understanding language, solving problems, and making decisions. The frontal lobe which provides the brain's executive function is the control center of the brain, the conductor of cognitive skills. Recent research has indicated that improved executive functioning is one of the major benefits of resistance training. Strength training has been related to improvement in memory and memory-related tasks and decision-making. These improvements may be attributed somewhat to increase in blood flow, higher levels of BDNF, and insulin-like growth factor stimulated by strength training. Resistance training has also been shown to have a positive effect on self-esteem, which gives the brain a boost, reducing the feelings of hopelessness and helplessness associated with depression. Resistance training is also associated with elevated mood.

ACSM Recommendations for Resistance Exercise

- Adults should train each major muscle group two or three days each week, using a variety of exercises and equipment.
- Very light or light intensity is best for older persons or previously sedentary adults starting exercise.
- Two to four sets of each exercise will help adults improve strength and power.
- For each exercise, 8 to 12 repetitions improve strength and power, 10 to 15 repetitions improve strength in middle age and older persons just starting an exercise program, and 15 to 20 repetitions improve muscular endurance.
- Adults should wait at least 48 hours between resistance training sessions.

#9: Add interval training to your exercise program to boost metabolism and maintain a healthy weight.

Interval training is alternating bursts of intense exercise with lighter activity. It is as simple as walking or jogging as fast as you can for up to 90 seconds and walking at a moderate pace for three to five minutes. It is cycling at an 8 or 9 on rate of perceived exertion (RPE) scale of 1 to 10 for up to 90 seconds then cycling at a 5 or 6 RPE for three to five minutes.

Interval training can boost your metabolism by burning more calories during the higher intensity intervals. The high intensity intervals should be anaerobic (above the training heart rate zone) for a short period of time. Anaerobic means "without oxygen," so your body doesn't deliver enough oxygen to the muscles during that time. The oxygen has to be paid back with interest, just like taking a loan from the bank. That means that the body will burn more calories for a period of time after the workout, too.

Interval training will also improve the body's ability to take in, transport, and use oxygen. The body will be able to do the high-intensity activity for longer periods of time as it adapts to the higher intensity intervals. The longer the high-intensity intervals are, the more calories burned.

Interval training can also add variety to the workout. Varying exercise routines can reduce boredom. The variations in intensity can also add a cross training element to an exercise program. Cross training challenges the body and brain to become more fit.

iStockphoto/Thinkstock

#10: Stretch to increase cerebrospinal fluid flow to crucial areas of the brain.

One of the body's reactions to stress is to contract muscles and tendons. This puts stress on joints and makes it more difficult for chemical messengers to get necessary information to, from, and within the brain. Tight lower back muscles in particular, reduce the flow of cerebrospinal fluid to the brain. Stretching releases the contraction of muscles and allows the fluid carrying messages through the central nervous system to flow more freely. Flexible and relaxed muscles, joints, and tendons are able to send information to the brain more efficiently. Stretching and lengthening exercises facilitate information from the brain stem area to the frontal lobes (the reasoning and problem-solving area of the brain).

Tight muscles also cause physical pain, which wears on the body and the brain. When the body hurts, the brain's attention is drawn to that pain, making it difficult to think.

ACSM Recommendations for Flexibility Exercise

- Adults should do flexibility exercises at least two or three days each week to improve range of motion.
- Each stretch should be held for 10 to 30 seconds to the point of tightness or slight discomfort.
- Repeat each stretch two to four times, accumulating 60 seconds per stretch.
- Static, dynamic, ballistic, and proprioceptive neuromuscular facilitation (contract-relax) stretches are all effective.
- Flexibility exercise is most effective when the muscle is warm. Try light aerobic activity or a hot bath to warm the muscles before stretching.

#11: Practice yoga to improve mood and decrease anxiety.

Yoga is an ancient practice, originating in India more than 5,000 years ago. Yoga began as a mental and physical exercise program designed to prolong life, enhance health, and promote personal growth. *Yoga* means "to join" the mind and body.

According to the American Yoga Association, hundreds of different forms and schools of yoga practice exist. The most common yoga practice is hatha yoga. YogaFit® has grown in popularity as a cross-training practice for fitness enthusiasts. Yoga improves muscle strength, endurance, and flexibility. Yoga also has a positive effect on balance.

Yoga increases levels of gamma-aminobutyric acid (GABA). GABA is the target of drugs (like Xanax®) that are used to relieve anxiety. GABA levels have been found to increase 27 percent after a 60-minute yoga session. Increased GABA levels create a calming effect on the body. Drugs used to reduce anxiety also increase GABA levels.

Yoga practice focuses attention with breathing. Focus on the breath creates a calming effect on the body. Yoga also focuses the mind, clearing it of chatter and increasing ability to concentrate.

Taking a yoga class can help to develop a network with others interested in improving health and fitness through the practice of yoga. Many yoga videos and books are available to build a practice of yoga at home. Living Arts, YogaFit, and Collage Video are good resources for yoga videos. *Yoga Anatomy* and *Anatomy of Hatha Yoga* are two popular books.

#12: Do Pilates to enhance coordination of the mind, body, and spirit.

Joseph Pilates studied many kinds of self-development improvement systems and developed the exercise known today as Pilates. Joseph Pilates' famous quote "It is the mind that builds the body" is the foundation of Pilates practice. The practice of Pilates is often referred to as contrology, the complete coordination of body, mind, and spirit.

In a Pilates training session, clients are instructed to focus and connect the brain to the body, with an emphasis on breathing. The focused and conscious movement gradually becomes automatic. The breath serves as a gateway to conscious movement decisions. The breath is used before, during, and after each Pilates movement to enhance coordination and mind-body control. The breath connects the body as it moves; the conscious movement gradually becomes automatic or subconscious as you develop muscle memory or muscle engrams. The spiritual aspect of Pilates may be different for everyone. It may be as simple as meditative time in the Pilates practice.

A variety of options to practice Pilates are available. The most popular is Pilates mat work, a series of Pilates foundational movements and exercises that require only a mat for equipment. Pilates mat work can be done in a Pilates center, fitness club, or at home with Pilates instructional DVDs or books. Pilates centers have specialized equipment and provide one-on-one and small group exercise training options.

iStockphoto/Thinkstock

#13: Try Tai Chi to put meditation in motion while learning invigorating motor sequences.

Tai Chi consists of slow-flowing, choreographed meditative movement. Tai Chi is an effective form of training as it combines complex, learned, motor sequence and requires a great deal of focus. This slow and meditative movement can be beneficial for people of all ages.

Mindful movement, focused breathing, attention, visualization, and rich psychosocial interactions with teachers and other students are all key components of Tai Chi. Each of these components plays a valuable role in improving brain health. One study found that people who practice Tai Chi three times a week did better on memory tests than those who did not. These people also had increases in brain volume.

Tai Chi can also play a role in fall prevention, reducing the risk of falls by 40 percent. Falls lead to fractures and breaks. Falls also can be associated with brain damage from the impact of the fall.

To successfully engage in Tai Chi, learn a small number of moves at a slow pace to understand and feel comfortable with them. Master a short and powerful series of moves that can easily fit a busy schedule. Stick with that series, and slowly add new movement to the series.

Check out the Tai Chi offered at local fitness centers and YMCAs, or learn Tai Chi at home with DVDs led by Tai Chi leaders like David Dorian Ross, Dr. Keith Jeffrey, or Scott Cole. Collage Video and Amazon are good resources for finding a Tai Chi video for beginner, intermediate, and advanced levels.

Duncan Smith

#14: Develop the core to guard the body and brain against falls and to improve posture.

Strengthening core muscles will contribute to boosting brain power by improving stability, balance, and posture. The core refers to the muscles of the abdominal and lower back regions. Core training means exercising those muscles, tendons, and ligaments that connect your spine and pelvis area around the center of your body. The main four muscle groups that make up the abdominal area include the rectus abdominis, internal and external obliques, and transverse abdominis. The core muscles of the back include the erector spinae, quadratus lumborum, and the multifidus.

Pilates training refers to the core as the powerhouse. Breathing is a main focus of training the powerhouse; focusing on contracting the core muscles during inhalation and especially on exhalation is a great start to strengthening the core. As you exhale, blow the air out of the mouth and continue the exhalation until you have expelled the air as completely as you can. Many Pilates mat training videos can be found on the market. Mari Winsor and Moira Stott are well-recognized Pilates instructors.

Yoga exercises that are particularly good for the core include the V-sit, spinal balance, plank, locust, and warrior three. The variety of good resources for safe and effective yoga practice includes: YogaFit, Living Arts, and GAIAM. Karen Voight also has a very good yoga DVD.

Effective core exercises can be done standing, seated, supine (on your back facing upward), and prone (on your front facing downward). Crunches are one of the most common exercises to train the core. Performing core exercises on a stability ball is one of the best ways to engage the core.

A good source for Pilates, yoga, and core training DVDs is Collage Video. Their website identifies beginner, intermediate, and advanced training levels. ACE-certified instructors preview videos and select only the best. The company has been in business for over 25 years and provides an excellent service in helping to find the best exercise DVD for your needs.

#15: Get involved in group exercise to music because it reduces your sense of fatigue so that you are able to work harder and longer.

Group exercise to music is a great option for three compelling reasons. First, you are in a group so there is a social component for better brain health. Second, you are exercising so you are moving your body, and because you are in a group you may push yourself a little bit more and find more enjoyment from being with a group of like-minded peers. Third, exercise to music typically increases intensity and duration of exercise.

Music promotes movement in a variety of ways. Music that is familiar, upbeat, and enjoyable to the listener reduces feelings of fatigue and lowers rating of perceived exertion to increase intensity and duration of the workout. Music can also be a form of arousal that inspires the listener to exert more effort and energy.

A wide variety of group exercise options are available. Group strength training, kickboxing, circuit training, boot camp, Zumba Fitness, interval training, yoga, Tai Chi, Pilates, and spinning are some of the popular choices. When selecting a group exercise program, look for programs with certified group exercise leaders. It is also important to choose classes that are appropriate for current level of fitness, interests, and ability. Start with beginner classes, and as fitness and skill levels improve, proceed to intermediate or advanced classes.

iStockphoto/Thinkstock

#16: Play sports as a way to connect with others and challenge your cerebellum with complex movement patterns.

Playing sports develops social skills, fosters relationships, and connects the brain and body with complex movement at all ages and stages of life. Athletes learn to make rapid assessments under stressful conditions with a wide range of variables. Sports can challenge the brain to improve problem-solving, split-second decision-making abilities, timing, self-discipline, and risk management. Sport involves high-level perceptual motor skills, assessment of risk, and, ultimately, skill execution (both body and mind).

The cerebellum works closely with the visual system, interprets the incoming information, and responds by making appropriate muscle movement. The more complex the movement, the more challenging the process—from input to feedback to correction. The more sophisticated the processing, the more areas of the brain are engaged, strengthening connections throughout the brain.

Golf, bowling, tennis, basketball, soccer, football, swimming, volleyball, gymnastics, dance, and wrestling are among the many sports that can connect brain and body. Choose a sport that is enjoyed and works best for personal fitness level, skill, ability, and age and stage of life.

Stockbyte

#17: Perform balance activities that will strengthen the vestibular system and connect the visual, spatial, and motor areas of the brain.

Balance requires the coordination of many systems of the body. The vestibular system works closely with the visual system to maintain balance and to coordinate head and eye movement. Proprioception is the ability to know where the body is in space. Specialized cells in the muscles, joints, and tendons work closely with the visual and vestibular system to help to monitor the position of the body. Many good exercises can improve the ability of these systems to work together to improve balance:

- Stand with the feet hip-width apart. For safety purposes, a hand should be placed on a stable surface until a person feels comfortable. Alternately, close one eye and then the other. If you feel stable, close both eyes.

- Place one hand on a stable surface while in a standing position. Engage the core muscles and alternately lift one foot and then the other off the ground. Remove the hand from the surface when comfortable. Hold each position for about 10 seconds. Close one eye and then the other to increase the challenge. Closing both eyes will make these systems work harder to keep the body in balance. Remove the hand from the surface for additional challenge.

- Sit on a stability ball with the feet hip-width apart. Engage the core muscles so that the spine is in a neutral position. Place the hands, palms forward, out to the side of the body at 5:00 p.m. and 7:00 p.m. Increase the challenge by alternating closing one eye and then the other eye. Closing both eyes will make the systems work even harder to keep the body in balance on the stability ball.

Tai Chi, yoga, and Pilates are good exercises to develop balance. Sue Scott's *ABLE Bodies Balance* training book includes 130 balance training exercises. Debra Rose's *Fall Proof* is another book with valuable balance training exercises. Many balance training DVDs suggest using BOSU® balls to improve the connection between the brain and body by staying in balance on an unstable surface.

#18: Take the stairs as a way to add fitness into your life while energizing your brain and strengthening your lower body.

The number-one excuse for not exercising is "I don't have time." You can add fitness into your life in many ways. Taking the stairs is one of the best. Stepping is one of the top five exercises for the lower body, and taking the stairs engages the same muscles. The gluteus maximus, medius, and minimus muscles are the large muscles upon which you sit and the muscles most engaged when climbing stairs. These large muscles need lots of oxygen to move consistently. Walking the stairs increases number of calories burned, and more oxygen is transported through the body and brain. Walking stairs also improves lower body strength. Walk up and down the steps at a slow, moderate, and fast pace to challenge the body in different ways. Take two steps at a time going up to add variation. If you have stairs in your workplace or home, make use them often to get you to other building levels and to fit fitness into your life while energizing your brain and making your lower body stronger.

Kane Skennar

#19: Plant a garden to lower levels of the stress hormone cortisol while improving mood and burning up to 300 calories an hour.

A comparison of a group of recreational gardeners working outdoors for a half-hour and a group who read indoors for a half-hour indicated that gardeners got a mood boost that the readers didn't experience. Gardening reduces the stress hormone cortisol, which helps to lower stress and improve mood while burning calories. These benefits are due to the affects of time in nature along with the physical activity. According to the American Council on Exercise, gardening activities like digging, hoeing, raking, and hauling garden supplies can burn an average of 300 calories an hour. These activities also develop muscle strength and endurance.

Gardening is associated with fresh air, exercise, and a sense of purpose. A gardener plants a seed, nurtures the seed, and has the pleasure of seeing plant growth. Many programs implement horticulture therapy in delivery of mental health care.

Gardening has been associated with a 50 percent reduction in dementia risk among older adults. Gardening is implemented in some schools to enhance overall life skills, ability to work in groups, and self-understanding. Gardening benefits all ages and stages of life.

Gardeners are more likely to eat their veggies and fruits than non-gardeners. Eating veggies and fruits packed with antioxidants can help to protect the brain. Dark-colored vegetables like spinach, broccoli, and red bell pepper have the highest levels of antioxidants, so enjoy the veggies and your labor by gardening for better brain health.

Comstock

#20: Improve brain efficiency with exercise.

Brain function becomes more efficient with regular exercise partially due to an increase in brain chemicals that help the brain to make connections. The key proteins that travel through the blood vessels to the brain when you move your muscles during physical activity play a major role. For instance, insulin-like growth factor (IGF-1) works along with human growth hormone to stimulate cell growth and prevent cell deterioration. Vascular endothelial growth factor (VEGF) along with fibroblast growth factor (FGF-2) signal cells to start dividing to make more blood vessels. Scientists have also discovered that VEGF is involved in cementing memories. Brain-derived neurotrophic factor (BDNF) is one of the most prominent chemicals that maintain brain cell circuits. Neuroscientists have referred to BDNF as fertilizer for the brain because of the role it plays in growing the neuron's dendritic branches. BDNF improves cell function while strengthening and protecting neurons from cell death. Exercise to increase levels of important brain chemicals that improve brain efficiency. Research indicates that aerobic exercise makes the biggest difference in boosting brain chemicals.

ACSM Recommendations for Cardiorespiratory Exercise

- Adults should get at least 150 minutes of moderate-intensity exercise per week.
- Exercise recommendations can be met through 30 to 60 minutes of moderate-intensity exercise (five days per week) or 20 to 60 minutes of vigorous-intensity exercise (three days per week).
- One continuous session and multiple shorter sessions (of at least 10 minutes) are both acceptable to accumulate desired amount of daily exercise.
- Gradual progression of exercise time, frequency, and intensity is recommended for best adherence and least injury risk.
- People unable to meet these minimums can still benefit from some activity (some activity is better than none).

#21: Play Wii sports and fitness games with friends and family to increase movement and activate brains during social gatherings.

When family and friends, get together the main activity is typically consumption of a large meal. Oxygen-rich blood is sent to the stomach to digest the food after you eat. Because less oxygenated blood is flowing to the brain, it is common to sit around or take a nap. Many people also feel cold because of reduced flow of blood to the skin. Getting up to move will get blood flowing to warm the body, energize the brain, and burn calories.

Wii sport and fitness games are great activities to get people up and moving around. Wii games provide a mild workout and are a better choice than sedentary video games or watching TV. Wii Sports provide a better overall body workout than Wii Fit. In Wii Sports, there is more jumping around, and the participants are not restrained by having to stand on a balance pad. The increased freedom of movement provides a better workout and burns more calories.

The remote control and almost unlimited channel options along with continual growth in video gaming options has led to people watching TV and playing video games for an average of 25 hours per week. Wii Sports and fitness is a good option to increase movement and get the body and brain engaged while interacting socially with other participants.

Wii Fit games provide four traits (goals, rules, feedback system, and voluntary participation) that create a physiology of positive emotions to further enhance the brain benefits. The goal provides focus. The rules increase creative and strategic thinking, collaboration, and teamwork. The frequency of feedback from the games increases motivation. Because participation is voluntary, the buy-in from the players creates a sense of camaraderie.

#22: Move your joints through a full range of motion to stimulate fluids that strengthen neuromuscular connections, thereby facilitating safe and fluid body movement.

Good flexibility is associated with safe and fluid body movement, which is a key component of fall prevention. Flexibility is also key to good posture, prevention of injuries and low back pain, alleviation of stress, and overall better body functioning. Healthy and flexible joints facilitate good communication between the body and brain. Although muscle flexibility is one of the most important components of fitness, stretching is one of the most disregarded.

iStockphoto/Thinkstock

Moving the joints through a full range of motion is good for the brain and the body. Dynamic stretching involves moving the joint through a full range of motion. Static stretching takes the muscle to the point of tightness at a joint, and holds that stretch for 10 to 30 seconds. Stretching releases synovial fluid stored in the joints. Synovial fluid lubricates the joints and promotes the transport of nutrients and chemicals necessary for the brain to communicate effectively with the joints, tendons, and muscles. Synovial fluid also lubricates all joints, protecting them from friction and injury.

It is best to stretch warm muscles. A short walk can prepare the body for stretching. Yoga sun salutations, marching in place, or riding a stationary bike are a good option if you are stretching in your home and don't have access to a treadmill.

Simple Dynamic Joint Lubricating Exercises

- *Ankles:* Lying on your side or back, seated or standing (standing takes more core strength and can improve balance), with one foot on the ground, lift one leg, and slowly rotate your suspended ankle in a circular motion in one direction and then the other. Point your toes to the floor and then up to the ceiling. Repeat with opposite leg.
- *Knees:* Lying on your side or back, seated or standing, lift one leg, and bend and straighten at the knee. Repeat with the other leg.
- *Hips:* Lying on your side, seated or standing, make a circle with the leg in one direction and then the other. Move through a full range of motion, moving the leg forward and back. Repeat with the other leg. Rock the hips from side to side and front to back. Imagine that the hips are a bucket holding water, and you are gently pouring water out of each side of the bucket.
- *Shoulders:* Seated or standing, rotate the shoulder forward, up, back, and down in a continuous and fluid movement, imagining that you are drawing a small circle in the area beside your shoulder. Lift the shoulder up toward the ear, and drop it as far away from the ear as possible, gently dropping the head in the opposite direction. Repeat on the other side, and then move both shoulder together.
- *Wrists and Fingers:* Rotate the wrists in a circular motion in each direction. Reach the fingers up to the sun and then down toward the earth. Open and close the hands. Gently circle each finger and then the thumb.

#23: Sit in good posture to send a signal of strength and confidence to the brain and to optimize space for organs in the abdominal area to work efficiently.

Sitting in chairs for more than 10 minutes can reduce concentration and attention. Sitting also takes a toll on the body, as spinal disc pressure is 30 percent greater when sitting versus standing. Sitting results in poor breathing and higher body fatigue. Most people sit with poor posture: leaning forward, rounding backs, and hunching shoulders. Poor sitting posture puts more pressure on the diaphragm and internal organs, restricting function, reducing blood circulation, and decreasing oxygen to the brain.

If you do have to sit for extended periods of time, an ergonomically correct chair can make a big difference. The angle between the legs and the spine should be between 120 and 135 degrees, halfway between sitting and standing. This posture provides balance between the front and back pelvis muscles.

It is also helpful to contract your abdominal muscles to keep your spine in a neutral position. Engaging your core muscles when you are sitting will improve strength and endurance while improving posture.

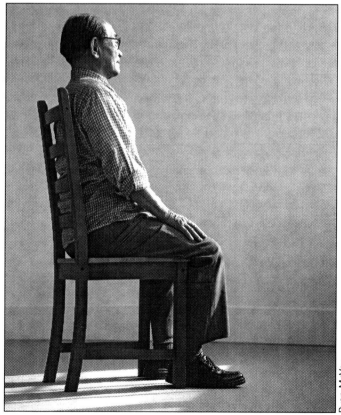

Ryan McVay

41

#24: Energize with Brain Gym movements that activate the brain for optimal storage and retrieval of information.

Brain Gym is committed to the principle that moving with intention leads to optimal learning. The Brain Gym educational model can be applied to all ages and stages of life and is designed to:

- Promote play and the joy of learning
- Draw out and honor innate intelligence
- Build awareness regarding the value of movement in daily life
- Emphasize the ability to notice and respond to movement-based needs
- Encourage self-responsibility
- Leave each participant appreciated and valued
- Empower each participant to better take charge of his own learning
- Encourage creativity and self-expression
- Inspire an appreciation of music, physical education, and the fine arts

Three energizing and effective Brain Gym movements include Brain Buttons, Cross Crawls, and Hook-Ups:

- *Brain Buttons* are done by placing one hand over the navel and the other hand between the ribs above the chest. The hand placed over the navel brings attention body's center of gravitation, where the core muscle are activated to contribute to body balance by alerting the vestibular system, which stimulates the reticular activating system waking the brain. The other hand gently rubs the space between the first and second ribs under the collarbone, to the right and left of the sternum. This is thought to stimulate blood flow through the carotid arteries.
- *Cross Crawls* can be done standing or sitting, crossing one arm across to the opposite knee as that knee is lifted. Repeat on the other side, and continue as if marching with the movement.
- *Hook-Ups* are done by first crossing one ankle over the other. The arms are then stretched out in front of you, with the back of the hands together and thumbs pointing down. Then, lift one hand over the other with the palms facing and interlock the fingers. Next, roll the locked hands straight down and in toward the body so they rest on the chest with the elbows down.

For more on Brain Gym, see www.braingym.org.

#25: Manage stress effectively to decrease levels of stress hormones, increase blood flow to the brain, decrease anxiety and depression, boost memory, and optimize brain functioning.

The fight-or-flight stress response is critical for survival, but chronic stress can be toxic to the body and the brain. The stress response is triggered by the perception of a threat. This threat is processed by the amygdala, which sends a message to the body to meet the demands of the situation with a release of stress hormones (norepinephrine, epinephrine, and cortisol) to increase heart rate, blood pressure, blood flow, and focus. The fight-or-flight response is to take care of immediate threat, but if the threat or perception of threat is persistent, the brain and body are negatively affected. Too much stress means decrease in blood flow to the brain, increased anxiety and depression, reduced memory, depressed immune system, and decreased memory. The hippocampus of the brain houses memory and is essential to learning. Chronic stress eats away at the dendrites and neurons in the hippocampus. The variety of ways to effectively manage stress includes the following:

- Take a walk.
- Practice yoga.
- Dance.
- Swim.
- Meditate.
- Eat a healthy diet.
- Get a massage.
- Talk to a friend.
- Listen to music.
- Change your point of view, embrace a positive perspective.

#26: Be aware of emotional, behavioral, physical, and cognitive stress symptoms (or signals) so you know when chronic stress is hurting your body and brain.

The human body works hard to stay in balance. Chronic stress is toxic to the body and the brain. Stress symptoms or signals alert the body and brain that stress is becoming harmful. Emotional stress symptoms may include avoidance of social situations, anxiety, depression, anger, or constant worry. Headaches, back and neck pain, stomach discomfort, and sleeplessness are common physical stress signals. Cognitive stress signals are forgetfulness that begins to interfere with productivity, inability to focus, and a general feeling of brain fog. Overeating, smoking, drinking too much, and substance abuse are common behavioral stress signals. They are the most challenging because they not only signal "too much stress, make some changes," they become habits that may be challenging to change.

Awareness is the first step to change; be aware of the signals, and then identify what is causing the stress. That means taking time to step back and think about what is going on in the workplace, school, or home life. Can the situation be changed? Is it possible to get out of the atmosphere for a break; sometimes, even a 10-minute walk can elevate the stress threshold and/or improve perception of a situation. It may be necessary to change perception if the cause of stress is going to be a permanent life fixture. Remember, there is no reality, only perception. Perceptions are the filters through which people see the world. Perceptions are affected by values, beliefs, experiences, knowledge, education, culture, community, and attitude. What stresses one person may have little to no effect on another person. Changing perception takes time and practice, but it is sometimes key to managing stress. Be aware of stress signals, and then take action.

#27: Think positively. Negative thinking releases toxic hormones in your body that will make your brain and your body unhealthy.

The power of thinking makes an incredible impact on the health of the brain and body. The biggest pharmacy is the one between your ears. You can think yourself into sickness with negative thinking or boost better health with positive thinking. Positive thinking elevates levels of feel good hormones like endorphins, while decreasing stress hormones like cortisol. Negative thinking releases the stress hormone cortisol in the body, triggering the fight-or-flight response, and typically increases anxiety, depression, high blood pressure, tense muscles, decreased blood circulation, and immune system dysfunction.

The first step to change is awareness. The mind thinks 50,000 to 60,000 thoughts a day. Each thought can change the physiology of the body, sending negative or positive chemicals throughout the body. Pay attention to positive and negative thoughts. Choose the filters through which you see the world. Filter the negative thoughts to the trash, or reshape those thoughts in a positive direction.

Following are a few of a variety of ways to get the mind off negative thoughts and redirect them in a positive direction:
- Read positive books.
- Listen to joyful music.
- Do a joyful dance.
- Watch a funny movie.
- Associate with positive people.
- Exercise.

It takes time to form a habit and many variables influence how much time it will take. Researchers suggest that it takes at least 66 days to form a new habit. If a person allows negative thoughts to consume thinking, a pattern of negative thinking becomes a natural pathway. Dr. Daniel Amen refers to this pattern as automatic negative thoughts (ANTs) and suggests the ANTs be stomped out and replaced with a positive thought. Reshaping the negative thought into a positive thought creates a pathway to positive thinking and better overall health.

The story of Norman Cousins surviving a life-threatening illness by focusing on the power of positive thinking and laughter is an important lesson to all. Cousin's case suggests that choosing a positive perspective can help or alter overall health and well-being.

#28: Use progressive relaxation to lower levels of stress hormones (like cortisol) in the body and to train the body to control the fight-or-flight response.

Cortisol and norepinephrine are the primary hormones released in stressful situations. They cause the body to respond to threat by increasing heart rate, blood pressure, and respiration. Toxic stress leads to increased levels of cortisol lingering in the body. Cortisol can eat away at brain cells (neurons), depress the immune system, increase anxiety and depression, and affect appetite. Progressive relaxation is an effective way to train the body to respond to threats that trigger the stress response while reducing the level of stress hormones in the body.

Progressive relaxation is a method of deep muscle relaxation developed in 1929 by Edmund Jacobson. The body responds to anxiety, provoking thoughts and events with muscle tension. The muscle tension increases anxiety. Progressive relaxation is the practice of consciously tensing and relaxing muscles. This technique can be practiced while lying on the back or in a seated position. Begin progressive relaxation with the eyes closed. Pay attention to the breath. The following is a simple example of the practice of progressive relaxation:

- Contract the muscles of the feet, holding the contraction for 5 seconds and then breathing deeply as the muscles relax and release for 20 seconds. Repeat as desired.
- Squeeze the muscles of the legs from the ankles to through the hips, contracting, contracting, and then after 5 seconds releasing for 20 seconds. Repeat as desired.
- Tense the muscles of the stomach and back, pressing the spine back against the floor or chair, squeezing for 5 seconds and then breathing deeply for 20 seconds to release. Repeat as desired.
- Tighten the muscles of the hand to create a fist and squeeze the muscles from the fingers and hands up through the shoulders. Hold the contraction for 5 seconds, and then gently release and relax the muscles of the hands, arms, and shoulders. Breathe deeply for 20 seconds. Repeat as desired.
- Engage and tense the muscle of the face and head for 5 seconds. Breathe and relax for 20 seconds. Repeat as desired.

Visualization can be effectively paired with progressive relaxation to maximize the experience. Visualizing a tranquil and happy place. Allowing the mind to wander and drift through natural environments on the beach, at a lake, or in the woods can enhance relaxation.

Audiotapes are available that can help an individual begin the practice of progressive relaxation. Amazon and the local library are good resources. With practice, progressive relaxation can make a difference in how the body responds to and balances life stressors.

#29: Practice breathing exercises to expand lung volume and increase blood flow to the brain, because the brain uses 20 percent of the body's oxygen.

The brain consumes more oxygen than any organ in the body. Breathing exercises can provide the brain with the oxygen it needs to work at optimal levels. Breathing exercises will enhance oxygen flow, reduce heart rate, and lower anxiety. Breathing exercises can reduce stress response by lowering blood pressure and slowing rate of breathing.

Many breathing exercises require no special equipment and can be done anywhere. Try different exercises to determine which work best for you. These exercises can be practiced with eyes closed or open.

- *Deep Sinking Breath:* The best position to practice this exercise is on your back, although this exercise can be done in a seated position. Option One: Take a deep breath in through your nose and exhale out of the nose, allowing your body to sink closer to the earth as you exhale. Option Two: Take a deep breath in through your nose and exhale out of the mouth, allowing your body to sink closer to the earth as you exhale. Repeat deep sinking breaths until you have allowed every muscle in the body to relax and release tension.
- *The Ten-Count Breath:* This exercise can be done seated or standing. Taking a deep breath in through the nose and exhale through the pursed lips as you count "1001, 1002, 1003, 1004, 1005, 1006, 1007, 1008, 1009, 1010." Repeat until you feel relaxed.
- *Breath Counting:* Seated in a comfortable position, gently close the eyes and take a few deep breaths, allowing the breath to come naturally in a slow and quiet manner. Begin the exercise by counting one as you exhale, count two on the next exhalation, continuing up to five. Then, begin a new cycle, counting one on the next exhalation. Try breath counting for 10 minutes as a form of meditation.
- *The Three-Part Breath:* The best position is on your back; however, three-part breathing can be practiced in a seated position. Taking a deep breath in through the nose, expanding the belly, the ribs, and the chest. Exhaling through the nose, relax the chest, the ribs, and the belly.
- *Pursed Lip Breathing:* Seated in good posture, breathe in through the nose. Purse lips slightly and slowly exhale through the pursed lips without forcing the air out. This is good approach to increasing lung volume and reducing anxiety and common stress responses.

#30: Minimize the stress in your life by not overcommitting.

Overcommitment in professional and personal lives is associated with increased feeling of stress, elevated muscle tension, reduced sleep, and higher anxiety. The fight-or-flight stress response causes the body to release cortisol and norepinephrine to meet the body's demands—real or perceived—to be able to perform. These stress hormones increase feelings of anxiety and also raise havoc with sleep patterns. As the brain and body work to keep up with an often overwhelming workload, muscles become tense and tight, creating another level of stress for the body to absorb.

Tips to Prevent Overcommitment and Reduce Stress

- *Identify priorities:* Time management is in large part about living life according to values. Identify your values, and look at how time is spent to determine if you are spending time on what is most important. For example, if you value physical fitness, you will make time for exercise; if you value family, you will spend quality time with family; if you value knowledge, you will spend time learning.

- *Be willing to delegate:* Let go of things that others can do or help you do. It may mean not getting things done just the way you think is best, but the same task can often be accomplished in many ways.

- *Avoid perfectionism:* Perfectionism often accompanies unwillingness to delegate. An obsession with things being perfect in itself can create a great deal of stress. Letting go of competition and judgment is a step toward lowering expectations of "perfect."

- *Say "No":* Practice the "Yes," "No," "Yes" strategy to saying "No" to avoid guilt and deliver the message with a positive approach. First, thank the person or people for thinking of you. Second, give a brief explanation of why you can't make another commitment. Third, thank the person again, and give them some ideas of someone else who may be willing to do the job, accept a smaller role in the job, or let them know that you really appreciate that they thought of you. It is a win-win approach to saying "No."

- *Let go of guilt:* There is no reason to feel guilty about taking care of personal health. It is often the people that are well-organized and always willing to go the extra mile who are the ones to do everything for everybody. Be proud of yourself for the strength to say "No." Remember the flight attendant's message: "In case of an emergency, an oxygen mask will drop; please secure yours before assisting others." If you don't take care of yourself, you put your health at risk and can't help others.

#31: Get adequate sleep to give the brain the time it needs to regenerate neurons and build memories.

Sleep helps in the formation of long-term memories. During sleep, the brain continues to work through the experiences of the day. The hippocampus, which is the keeper of short-term memory, is particularly active in replaying recent experiences during sleep. As the brain replays these memories, they can be transferred more efficiently to long-term memory. Storing memory for the long term requires sleep.

Sleeping less than a normal night's sleep negatively affects energy level, ability to think and learn, performance, alertness, reaction time, productivity, creativity, safety, health, longevity, and overall quality of life. The body clock is usually set by the daily pattern of sunrise and sunset. The body's clock can be disrupted by sickness and disease, travel, lifestyle choices, stress, and aging.

Sleep needs differ by individual. Most adults require seven to nine hours of sleep per night. Too much sleep can have negative health consequences and may be associated with depression. As an adult, determine the amount of sleep that works best for you by your personal health, happiness, and productivity.

iStockphoto/Thinkstock

Children ages 5 to 10 need approximately 10 to 11 hours of sleep. Adolescents have a sleep cycle different from older and younger individuals, typically going to bed later and waking later. It is recommended that teenagers get around nine hours of sleep nightly, but most get only seven. Most sleep researchers agree that the best school start time for kids is 8:30, and some schools are switching school schedules and seeing better school performance in middle school and high school students.

Tips Associated With Good Sleep

- Stick to a regular bedtime.
- Avoid caffeine for six hours prior to going to bed.
- Don't exercise within four hours of bedtime.
- Sleep in darkness.
- Read before sleeping.
- Don't play video games, watch TV, or work on computer before bed, the lights from these machines prevents the brain from releasing natural sleep chemicals.
- Avoid alcohol within three hours of bedtime.
- Don't eat a large meal late in the evening.
- Exercise during the day to sleep better at night.

Websites to Learn More About Quality Sleep

- www.sleepfoundation.org
- www.sleepapnea.org

#32: Take a nap to recharge your brain.

A 15- to 20-minute nap in early to mid afternoon can recharge your brain and body. Naps are good for everyone, but very beneficial for those who sleep only four to six hours. Napping is not sleeping. Napping is moving from beta waves to alpha waves. The electrical activity in the body is categorized by frequency of the waves. Beta waves are associated with wakeful alertness known as attention and arousal. Alpha waves are associated with quiet rest and meditation with eyes closed, alpha waves usually move to beta waves when eyes reopen. If the brain goes in to theta state, a light sleep, the body is then officially asleep and will more than likely will be groggy when the body wakes. The ideal length for naps is 10 to 30 minutes, and the best time is about six hours after waking for the day. Napping too late in the day may make it difficult to fall asleep at night. It is suggested that, for the sleep-deprived, napping improves performance but not mood, and for normal sleepers, napping improves mood and often performance. Napping can also boost creativity.

Tips for Napping

- Take a nap early to mid-afternoon.
- Close the eyes.
- Get comfortable but not so comfortable that the brain goes to sleep.
- Let the mind be empty or busy whatever it chooses, and try not to direct the thoughts.
- Keep the nap at 10 to 30 minutes in length.

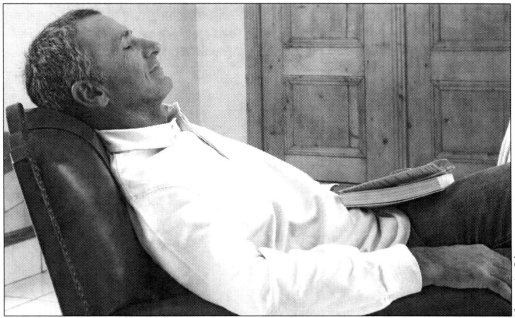

Vincent Le Prince

#33: Get a massage to increase mood-enhancing chemicals like serotonin and dopamine and lower the stress hormone cortisol.

Massage isn't just a way to pamper and rejuvenate the body. Massage is good for the body and the brain. It is estimated that 80 to 90 percent of illness and disease is directly related to stress. Lowering stress with massage can decrease anxiety and reduce depression, partially from an increase in levels of serotonin (the neurotransmitter vital for impulse control) and dopamine (the neurotransmitter key in drive and reward) and a decrease in the stress hormone cortisol. Massage also improves quality of sleep, which increases stress threshold and lowers anxiety and depression. The increased circulation that results from a massage will boost concentration and focus, another brain benefit of massage.

Massage can enhance overall health and well-being of the body and brain from infancy through your older years. Massage can alleviate back pain, improve range of motion and joint flexibility, stretch tight muscles, help repair muscles after or prepare muscles before a strenuous workout, relax tired and overused muscles, and enhance immunity by stimulating lymph flow.

Massage has been practiced for thousands of years, and you can find at least 80 massage therapy styles from which to choose. Among the most popular are Swedish massage, neuromuscular therapy massage, deep tissue massage, and sports massage. A massage can last anywhere from five minutes to two hours.

Massage therapists, physical therapists, or occupational therapists can perform massage. Ask your doctor or someone else you trust for a recommendation. Most states regulate massage therapists through licensing, registration, or certification requirements. Before booking a massage, find out which style the therapist uses, and let the therapist know what you want to accomplish for a customized massage.

#34: Disconnect from technology to allow the brain down time to go over experiences, solidify information, and convert information to long-term memory.

Watching television, channel surfing, Internet browsing, checking e-mails, and connecting with the many other social network options makes lives a little busier. It is a way to connect and a way to disconnect. Like many things, keeping a balance with how much time a person is connected with technology is healthy.

If you notice, for example, that you are carrying cell phone chargers with you and feel like your cell phone is an extension of your hand, it may be a good idea to turn it off and take a break. If you can't function for a day or even a few hours without your cell phone, you may want to take a nature break.

The vast amount of technology available today has created a new world. As with anything else, everything cyberspace can connect you to in the world has its good and bad points. Because it is at their fingertips, people are often multitasking at all times. The brain will do its best work when focused on a task. If the brain is watching TV, checking social media, and working on a project, it is less productive and not as likely to be able to filter out irrelevant information. The majority of brains can't pay attention to that much stimuli.

New addictions—like nomophobia or mobile phone addiction—are growing in numbers. Symptoms of nomophobia include panic and anxiety when separated from the phone, having multiple phones, compulsively checking the phone, and phone activity affecting relationships.

Taking time each day to disconnect from technology allows time for the brain to reflect on experiences, solidify information, make connections, and convert short-term memory to long-term memory. Disconnecting from technology can help the brain to strengthen connections.

#35: Talk to someone to disengage from negative thinking or worry.

Negative thinking and worry + isolation = more negative thinking and worry. The term *rumination* refers to negative contemplation or reflection, which may become persistent, recurrent worrying or brooding. Rumination is turning a matter over and over in the mind, a gerbil wheel in the brain that can create anxiety and sadness. The negative thinking pattern will actually affect the cells of the human body in a negative way, too.

One of the best ways to change thinking is to talk to a friend, colleague, family member, or mental health professional, preferably a positive person. One very good way to change perception is to get perspectives from others. Each situation can be seen in a variety of ways, and different perspectives can help to change thinking. Positive thought control is a healthy way to train the brain.

Talking to someone else can also get the mind off the issues that are controlling negative thoughts and worry and help to focus thoughts on different things. Getting out of the house or office and socializing is one of the best ways to lighten a mood and distract from rumination.

Jack Hollingsworth

#36: Listen to music to improve mood, lower the stress response, boost the immune system, enhance exercising, fight fatigue, and increase productivity.

Music can help people to relax, relieve stress, elevate mood, and increase motivation. Artists like George Winston and Jim Brickman play piano music that can be soothing and help the body relax. Instrumental music and music with environmental sounds is often used in yoga classes to set a calm feeling tone. Studies have shown that music can even be effective in lowering blood pressure and heart rate. Music can be an effective therapy.

Upbeat music with positive messages can improve mood. Music associated with the era in which an individual was in middle school through college years tends to create positive energy. Music can also affect people negatively. Rap and heavy metal music with negative messages can actually make people angry. Listening to a sad song can make a person sad, and listening to a happy song can make a person happy.

Music can increase the duration and intensity of exercise. The tempo of the music will usually set the pace for the exercise. The energy level of the music can affect both duration and effort in an exercise session. It is easy to create a high-energy music mix for an mp3 player. Another option is purchasing music mixes designed by companies specializing in designing music mixes for group exercise. The following websites have great exercise music mixes for all ages and stages of life:

- www.dynamixmusic.com
- www.powermusic.com
- www.yesfitnessmusic.com

Listening to music while walking, running, lifting weights, or participating in group exercise can help to set an energetic pace and affect how hard an individual works.

#37: Laugh to boost the immune system, reduce muscle tension, and release endorphins, the "feel-good hormones" in your brain.

Norman Cousins hired a nurse to read him funny stories and watched Marx Brothers movies to laugh himself to wellness. Cousins found that laughter helped him to sleep and relieved pain. Laughter produces endorphins, the body's natural painkiller. Laughter is also known to enhance respiration, increase number of immune cells, decrease cortisol levels, and lower blood pressure.

Lee Berk's SMILE questionnaire can give you an idea of how much you use laughter to stay in balance. You can search online for Lee Berke and SMILE or go to www.natural-humor-medicine.com/humor-quiz.html to check out your laughter score and get ideas on how to add humor to your life.

Surround yourself with people who make you laugh and look at the brighter side of life. Spend time with people who can make you smile from head to toe, avoid those who make you smile only when they are walking away. Taking life too seriously can have a detrimental effect on the brain and the body.

A variety of humor resources can be found on the Internet. Joke-of-the-day sites and e-mail options can provide you with a good laugh every day. Countless comic strips, books, magazines, and audios are available that can provide hours of humorous entertainment. Sense of humor can be consciously improved and developed to add laughter to your brain and body wellness regimen.

> *The human race has only one really effective weapon,*
> *and that's laughter. The moment it arises, all our*
> *hardnesses yield, all our irritations and resentments*
> *slip away, and a sunny spirit takes their place.*
> —Mark Twain

#38: Enjoy nature. Natural surroundings allow the brain to renew and replenish.

Taking a walk in a quiet park or on a hiking trail along a beautiful hillside can allow the brain to decide what to pay attention to without cell phones ringing or e-mails beeping for response. The natural setting allows the brain to restore the ability to direct attention while giving time for working memory connections (which are developed in the hippocampus) to be formed.

A nature-based environment is associated with lower blood pressure and reduced levels of the stress hormone cortisol. Exercising outdoors is an excellent way to maximize the benefits of nature on the body and brain. Grounding the mind with gardening is good exercise and an excellent way to connect with nature. Eating the fresh fruits and vegetables from that garden will provide the body and brain with key nutrients. Green grass, plants, trees, a beach, a river stream, or a mountain view can have calming effects on the mind and body.

Inhibition is a crucial brain regulatory function. It is important for the brain to be able to divert brain energy stores away from distractions and toward important attentional tasks. In today's world, the brain has to work overtime because the multitude of distractions makes it difficult for the brain to filter out distractions. For example, the pop-ups and advertisements on a website or the buzz of cell phone receiving a text. Consider the 100 or more TV channels to choose from compared to three or four in the 1960s and 1970s. With so many things pulling for attention, the brain can experience directed function fatigue, an inability to focus on key.

Studies have shown elevated mood in people taking a walk in the park in comparison to a walking along busy city streets. Green space, being out in nature, improves mental outlook and reduces the stress burden on the body. Time in natural surroundings, like a park or hiking trail along hills or mountains, can refresh and renew the brain. Even looking out a window at green trees, green grass, and flowers can elevate mood and boost ability to work more efficiently and effectively.

#39: Eat a healthy diet for a healthy brain. What and how you eat is crucial to brain health.

A variety of foods are boosters for the brain and the body. The basics include the following:

- Colorful vegetables that are rich in antioxidants (Dark green, deep orange, and yellow are the best to consume.)
- Whole grain foods that have high fiber and lots of nutrients: brown rice, whole wheat bread, oats
- Fresh or frozen fruits like blueberries, strawberries, oranges, and cherries
- Protein from fish, lean meats, salmon (AHA recommends eating fish at least two times a week.)
- Low-fat milk and yogurt
- Foods high in omega-3 fats: salmon tuna, olive oil, canola oil, green leafy vegetables, lean meats
- Nonfat and low-fat dairy products

Foods that can have an adverse affect on body and brain health include the following:

- Those with excess saturated fat: cheese, fried foods
- Foods high in trans fats: margarine, chips, fast foods
- Refined carbohydrates like white rice, white bread, pasta, cookies, candy
- Foods high in sodium, try to keep sodium to a teaspoon a day

How people eat makes a difference, too. Eating on the go typically results in eating more highly processed foods and eating quickly, often consuming more calories than necessary. Eating in front of the TV usually results in overeating. Eat small meals more often rather than two or three large meals. Large meals are more difficult to digest and often result in a tired feeling that decreases activity after the meal.

#40: Chew more, and eat less. It takes the brain up to 20 minutes to register that the stomach is full. Healthy weight = healthy brain and body.

The brain and stomach register the feeling of fullness after approximately 20 minutes. If a person eats quickly, the hormones released by the intestines that inform the brain that the body has received enough food don't have time to signal "full." The hormone leptin is one of the hormonal regulators that needs time to relay that information. Leptin works with dopamine to provide a feeling of fullness and satisfaction from consuming enough food.

Research supports the claim that when meals are eaten more slowly, significantly fewer calories and more water are consumed. People tend to eat more quickly if they wait too long between meals without a healthy snack. It is important to keep in mind that eating foods with high sugar content increases appetite. Recent studies reveal that people given 300 calories of soda at a meal also eat 300 extra calories during that meal.

Tips to Chew More, and Eat Less

- Eat a healthy snack an hour or so before meals.
- Chew 30 times before swallowing food.
- Always eat breakfast.
- Don't eat past 8:00 p.m. (rule of thumb: if you eat after 8:00, you'll gain weight).
- Time your eating; be conscious of not gobbling your food in five minutes.
- Put your eating utensil down after every bite.
- Drink water before, during, and after your meal.
- Eat with your nondominant hand.
- Don't eat while watching TV; you don't pay attention to how much you eat.
- Eat to slow and relaxing music.
- Increase your awareness of chewing and enjoying your food.
- Set aside 20 to 30 minutes to eat slowly and take pleasure in your meal.
- When you feel full, remove the food from in front of you.

#41: Drink water (approximately 80 percent of the brain is water). Dehydration leads to limited ability to concentrate and make decisions.

Dehydration is a common problem that's linked to poor learning. A high percentage of the brain is made up of water, so lack of water takes a toll very quickly. Water is an instant brain booster. Drinking water improves concentration and increases energy levels. Water is a natural conductor of electricity. Each neuron in the brain sends out an electrical response when one cell communicates to another. Approximately 10 minutes after drinking water, an improvement in retention and memory retrieval can occur. Drinking water helps to lower stress hormones in as quickly as five minutes.

If you eat a healthy diet, about 20 percent of your water will come from the foods you eat. It is recommended that a person drink one third of an ounce of water per pound of body weight each day and that amount should be doubled in time of stress. Online hydration calculators can give estimates on daily recommended water intake.

Polka Dot Images

#42: Fuel your brain with a healthy breakfast to provide the glucose it needs for optimal functioning as you begin your day.

Breakfast means "break the fast." Eating breakfast gives you a mental and physical advantage as it restores the glycogen levels necessary to think and to move. Not eating a healthy breakfast has the following consequences:

- Skipping breakfast leads to a reduction in cognitive functioning because the brain doesn't get the glucose it needs to do its work. The brain uses 20 percent of the body's energy, and that energy is in the form of glucose. Children who do not eat breakfast usually have lower test scores, more difficulty focusing, increased behavior issues, and poor attendance and tardiness issues.
- Skipping breakfast decreases energy levels and will increase lethargic behaviors. If a person doesn't eat breakfast, it will be more challenging to participate in physical activity. If blood sugar levels are too low, it is dangerous to exercise and dizziness or fainting may occur.
- Skipping breakfast also leads to weight gain, as it is common practice to overeat and make poor food choices due to excessive hunger.

A nutritious breakfast should include complex carbohydrates and protein. A hard-boiled egg, oatmeal and dried raisins, and fruit (or a high-fiber cereal and fruit) are a few healthy options. Some people don't like typical breakfast foods, so a nontraditional option like grilled chicken breast and vegetables are another good start to energizing the brain and body to "break the fast." If you're on the go and don't have time for a sit-down breakfast, grab a banana and take some almonds with you to snack on throughout the morning.

#43: Maintain a healthy weight. People who are obese have twice the risk of developing dementia.

Obesity leads to a variety of health-related diseases, including dementia. Fatty tissue is the largest hormone-producing organ in the body, and it can produce inflammatory molecules, which may affect cognitive functioning and the process of neurodegeneration, progressive loss of structure and function, including death of neurons. The health-related diseases associated with obesity further increase risk of dementia and Alzheimer's.

Increase in body fat puts a great deal of stress on the cardiovascular system; increasing blood pressure and risk for heart disease. The cardiovascular system has a more challenging time delivering blood to the brain. The blood carries oxygen and glucose necessary for the brain to function effectively and efficiently. The brain uses 20 percent of the body's oxygen and glucose, so decreased blood flow to the brain has a significant effect on brain function.

Obesity is associated with insulin-dependent diabetes. The brain needs glucose to function effectively. Insulin provides the lock and key mechanism for bringing the necessary sugar to the brain for neurons to get the energy necessary to fire efficiently.

Regular exercise and a healthy diet are the two key lifestyle choices that are necessary for maintaining a healthy weight. Maintain a caloric balance, not consuming more calories than burned. Many online calorie calculators can help you determine how many calories your body needs or burns through various activities. Check out www.caloriesperhour.com/index_burn.php as one option. Taking your body weight times 12 gives a very rough estimate of calories burned in a day without taking activity or fitness levels into consideration.

#44: Watch portion sizes and avoid supersizing to avoid unnecessary weight gain. Eating too much in one meal reduces oxygen flow to the brain.

The body sends oxygen where it is most needed. When a large meal is consumed, oxygen-rich blood goes to the stomach to aid in the digestion of the food. As a result, less oxygenated blood is going to the brain and to the muscles. A tired, lethargic feeling typically follows overeating because of that change in blood flow.

Bigger portions and supersizing are in great part the culprit of obesity. Portion or serving sizes are general guidelines that can be followed to keep caloric intake healthier. Using the following simple estimates of a serving is a good start to portion control and healthy weight management:

- A small baked potato is the size of a computer mouse.
- One cup of broccoli, carrots, popcorn, pasta, leafy greens, or strawberries, a medium apple, or a cup of soup or chili is the size of a baseball.
- One cup of cooked rice or beans or a half cup of blueberries or grapes is the size of a light bulb.
- Three ounces of lean beef or cooked chicken is the size of a deck of cards.
- One tablespoon of butter, margarine, or mayonnaise is the size of a poker chip.
- Three ounces of grilled fish is the size of a checkbook.
- A slice of pizza is the size of two one-dollar bills.

These visuals are good guides for portion control. Another good visual and eye-opener is the movie *Super Size Me*. Some people have the belief that spending the extra 25 cents to get 25 to 50 percent more food is the real deal. Most people also have the belief that it is important to "clean the plate" (remember all those poor starving children in Africa, etc.?). These two beliefs link to associate weight gain with supersizing. Watching portion sizes and skipping the supersize option is good for the body and brain.

#45: Eat fruits and vegetables to reduce risk of cognitive impairment by reducing oxidative stress to the brain.

A wide variety of important nutrients, like vitamin C, vitamin E, beta-carotene, and selenium and compounds called carotenoids and flavonoids are found in fruits and vegetables. These antioxidants play an important role in protecting the brain and keeping it healthy throughout the aging process. Unstable oxygen molecules from tobacco smoke, pollution, and ultraviolet radiation damage cells through a process called oxidative stress. Eating many types of fruits and vegetables, especially lush colored ones, can prevent cognitive decline.

Antioxidants can be measured by what is known as oxygen radical absorbance capacity (ORAC) score. Foods high in antioxidants play an important role in prevention of cancer and cognitive decline.

Fruits with the highest antioxidant scores include blueberries, blackberries, red delicious apples with skin, and sweet cherries. Other high scorers include black plums, raspberries, cranberries, strawberries, navel oranges, and red grapes.

Vegetables high in antioxidant value include raw garlic, cooked red cabbage, and cooked broccoli. Carrots, yams, red peppers, sweet tomatoes, onions, sweet potatoes, and dark leafy greens like spinach are also very good antioxidants.

iStockphoto/Thinkstock

#46: Prevent low and high blood sugar for the brain to function at optimal level.

The brain uses 20 percent of the body's glucose. Low blood sugar levels (hypoglycemia) lead to mental confusion, difficulty making decisions, and inability to remember. Hypoglycemia affects hormonal and central nervous system functioning. Symptoms of hypoglycemia may begin with confusion that is accompanied by sweating, shaking, and nervousness. Dangerously low blood sugar can result in loss of consciousness.

High levels of blood sugar affect brain functioning throughout the lifespan. People with high blood sugar levels are likely to experience brain shrinkage in the hippocampus and amygdala. The hippocampus of the brain is the place where short-term memory is developed and stored. Death of neurons in the hippocampus means that it gets smaller, and the brain has less capacity for moving information from short-term memory to working and long-term memory. Decreased brain functioning has been linked to high blood sugar levels even in teen years. The decrease in cognitive functioning worsens if high blood sugar is persistent throughout the years. People with high blood sugar also have a high risk of dementia and Alzheimer's, as both are prevalent when hippocampus functioning is in decline. After controlling for age, high blood pressure, and smoking, high blood sugar can account for six to 10 percent of brain shrinkage.

The typical American diet is very high in sugar. Recommendations for a healthy diet are about 10 teaspoons or 40 grams of sugar a day. A cup of ice cream provides 60 percent of a day's worth of sugar and a 12-ounce non-diet cola provides 103 percent.

Awareness is one of the first steps to keeping blood sugars and caloric intake/ expenditure in balance. Keeping a food journal is one of the best ways to increase awareness of the kinds and amount of foods being consumed. Another key step to keeping healthy food choices is to distinguish between hunger and cravings. Hunger signals are your stomach's way of informing you that is empty. Stomach signals you may experience include growls, pangs, or hollow feelings. Brain signals that you are hungry could be headache, lack of concentration, or fatigue. Cravings are caused by physical or psychological needs. A body that consumes more sugar than necessary over time will crave those high levels of sugar. Eating high fat and high sugar comfort foods is common when stressed, worried, or sad.

#47: Consume omega-3 fatty acids, which are key in transmitting information in the brain.

Higher level of omega-3 essential fatty acids is associated with reduced risk of dementia and Alzheimer's. Omega-3 fatty acids promote efficient electrical signaling between neurons in the brain. Omega-3 fatty acids help stabilize cell membranes. Omega-3 fatty acids even appear to improve mental concentration and prevent memory loss. Omega-3s play a key role in reducing inflammation and limiting build-up of amyloid plaque that clogs the brains of Alzheimer's patients.

The body doesn't produce omega-3 fatty acids and needs to absorb them from food sources. Some of the best fish sources include salmon, sardines, herring, tuna, and mackerel. Flaxseeds are top source of omega-3s. Mixing flaxseed in breakfast cereals, muffins, or other baked goods is a great way to make them part of a daily diet. Walnuts and butternuts are the top nut choices for omega-3s. Olive oil and canola oil are the top choices for cooking and baking. Adding an avocado to salad or sandwich is another good way to boost omega-3 fatty acids—and brainpower.

iStockphoto/Thinkstock

#48: Stimulate the brain with a variety of mental activities for better brain health across the lifespan.

One of the key principles of exercise training is progressive overload. This principle states that in order to get stronger or have better cardiovascular endurance, there must be a safe overload to challenge the muscles and the cardiovascular system. It is best to increase the load or intensity progressively to continually improve. If an individual does the same thing over and over and over, the body adapts and does not improve. A reduction in muscle or cardiovascular fitness may result if an individual does the same activity weekly with no changes in exercises or type of equipment used.

The principle of progressive overload applies to keeping the brain healthy, too. It is important to learn different things, participate in different activities, and engage the brain in new and different ways to strengthen and make new connections in the brain. For instance, if a person does a great deal of reading and reads the same author or the same topic, the familiarity makes that author's style of writing very predictable or the information easy to remember. Reading new and different things, listening to an audiobook, or joining a book club to get a different perspective is a good way to get out of the box. If a person reads a great deal, but doesn't do mathematical activities, the language part of the brain is strengthened, but the math processing may need good workouts to become stronger and more efficient. Playing games that require simple math reasoning (like Yahtzee® or gin rummy) is an easy way to work on numbers to cross-train the brain.

A person can cross-train the brain by doing a variety of mental activities to engage different parts of the brain and strengthen different connections in the brain. Runners can swim to challenge different muscles to increase cardiovascular endurance. People who have strong verbal skills can strength math skills by doing puzzles, playing tic-tac-toe, playing cards, or doing math games available online. People who have stronger math skills can play games like Boggle®, Scrabble®, or the wide variety of interactive group games requiring verbal reasoning. Engaging in different mental activities boosts brainpower.

#49: Travel to introduce your brain to new places and different ways to get there to increase synaptogenesis (growth of connections between neurons).

Travel nurtures a healthy brain in a variety of ways. Traveling provides great experiences, both pleasant and challenging. Theses experiences build new memories that as stories are told, pictures are put in scrapbooks or slide shows, and relationships are formed lead to long-term memories. The emotional part of the brain strengthens the connections built by travel.

Traveling, especially on an unguided trip, engages the brain in valuable planning and problem solving that engages all the senses. The options, issues, and problems from transportation to scheduling engage the brain autopilot.

Traveling in a foreign country adds mental tasks like converting currency and navigating through different languages. New cultures have a way of engaging the brain to broaden perspective with a richer worldview. Taking a trip to a foreign country is like P90X® extreme workout training for the brain.

Taking a traveling vacation can also refresh the mind, body, and soul. The brain can get out of the box and shift thinking. Meeting new people can add an entirely new dimension to the traveling experiences. Social experiences from traveling are the nonfat icing on the brain boosting cake.

iStockphoto/Thinkstock

#50: Play sudoku to challenge the left hemisphere of the brain to find number patterns. Do crossword puzzles to challenge the language and memory areas of the brain.

Adults with hobbies that exercise the brain are less likely to get dementia or Alzheimer's. Sudoku, crossword puzzles, and word searches are excellent activities that can be easily become a daily activity that is considered "mental aerobics."

Sudoku is one of the best cognitive stimulating activities, as it requires a significant amount of concentration and attention. Sudoku particularly challenges the left side of the brain, as it is a game of logic. Sudoku helps train the brain to be efficient at abstract reasoning and quick thinking. The game is fun and a beginner can start with an easy puzzle and gradually progress to more challenging games. Sudoku games are found in weekly newspapers, magazines, and books. Sudoku can also be played online or downloaded and printed from websites like www.websudoku.com.

Crossword puzzles challenge the speech and language centers of the brain to find words. It is important to select crossword puzzles that are challenging enough to make the brain work. If the answers come without some thought and possibly a little bit of research, the brain isn't working hard enough to make a difference. It's like going on a one-mile walk every day for a year without changing the intensity. The body adapts and doesn't improve. If crossword puzzles aren't challenging, the brain adapts and doesn't improve. Crossword puzzles are also found in newspapers, magazines, and online (e.g., www.realage.com/better-memory/crossword-puzzles and www.kappapuzzles.com/alz/solveacrossword.html).

#51: Be aware of the effects of lighting and color on the brain.

Levels of light affect the brain. Abundant lighting helps the brain to pay attention and stay awake. Lower levels of light can make it more difficult for the brain to focus. A person also tends to become sleepier if lighting is low. A bright room creates a better learning environment. When lights need to be turned down when showing an overhead slide presentation, it is good practice to turn the lights back up when the visual aide is no longer being used. Doing an activity to get people moving after sitting in a darker room will also help to increase attention levels.

When daylight hours become more limited, some people experience seasonal affective disorder (SAD). Feelings of depression can increase when sunlight is limited. Mood is usually lifted when days become longer and the nights are shorter. Melatonin is released from the pineal glad when it is dark. Melatonin is a hormone that promotes sleep. If it is light all the time, lack of production of melatonin may disrupt sleep patterns.

Studies suggest that people respond differently to various colors. The response to red is increased creativity and short-term high energy. Green is associated with productivity and long-term energy. It is believed that green is good for the heart. Green is a color associated with nature and promotes physical equilibrium. The colors yellow, orange, or coral are more conducive to physical work and exercising; these colors are believed to elicit a positive mood. Blue slows pulse and a lower blood pressure and is creates a good environment for study and concentration. Purple and pink are colors that create a more calming and restful environment.

In general, it appears that bright lights and colors are more associated with higher energy levels. An environment of good light and bright colors may be more conducive to learning.

#52: Read a book, magazine, or newspaper to establish new connections in your brain.

Reading helps to make new connections in the brain. Reading demands more from the neuronal connections in the brain. Reading can also play a role in increasing knowledge, reducing stress, improving analytical thinking, increasing vocabulary, and improving writing skills. People who read typically have higher GPAs, intelligence, and general knowledge. Reading reduces stress by distracting the mind from troubles or worries. Reading helps a person to improve ability to identify patterns, boosting analytical thinking. As a person reads, vocabulary and critical thinking increases, especially as books become more challenging. With improved knowledge, analytical and critical thinking, and vocabulary, writing skills become more developed as well.

Books offer the reader more in-depth understanding about a certain topic. Magazines have the newest discussions and ideas on a variety of topics, providing a brief overview of a topic. Newspaper reading is on the most current topics and, like magazines, provides a brief overview of a topic from the writer's perspective. Reading from a variety of sources challenges thinking and establishes new connections. When a person watches a movie, it is as a spectator; when reading the story; the brain engages in creating the picture and the emotions.

Getting children off to a good start with decoding and word recognition skills are key to successful reading, and a strong start in reading is the foundation of an avid reader. Those who read well are more likely to read more. Providing and encouraging as many reading experiences as possible in younger years is also key in developing good skills and an interest in lifelong reading.

#53: Join a book club to challenge your brain to absorb the perspectives of others on things you read.

Book clubs are a very good way to develop friendships, read different books, and open the mind to the perspectives others have on book content. It may also create an incentive to read more, read different varieties of books, and become more open-minded.

The purpose of a book club meeting is to discuss the book of the month, or the book of the week. In that discussion, people learn a lot about each other. Good personal social networking time provides an opportunity for growing friendships. The book discussions draw many different perspectives of the reading and opens the minds to new perspectives while providing opportunities to learn of others' interests and perspectives.

Typically, each member of the book club selects a book or two throughout the year. This approach adds to variety in reading due to the different interests of and research done by group members. It is a great opportunity to read books a person may not consider reading.

Reality is based on perception. Each person reads a book through personal perspective. During book club meetings, it is common to hear a variety of perspectives throughout the discussions. People will have different insight that may open thinking to see not only the book, but also other life experiences from different perspectives. Book clubs are a great way to expand thinking and step out of the box.

#54: Pay attention to key numbers for better health.

Know Your Body Mass Index

Body mass index is a number that gives an indication of body fatness using height and weight. A healthy BMI is 18.5 to 24.9; overweight is 25 to 29.9; obese is greater than 30. A number of online calculators can be used to calculate BMI.

Know How Many Calories Your Body Needs

A pound of fat contains 3,500 calories. A pound of fat is gained if a person consumes 3,500 calories more than needed. A pound is lost if a person burns 3,500 more than

IT Stock

consumed. Many online calculators help to estimate daily caloric needs based on height, weight, age, and activity level. One recommended website is: www.acefitness.org.

Know How Many Calories You Consume

Many online calculators can help track how many calories are in foods. You can also find books that provide information on calories in foods. It can be time-consuming to look up and chart caloric consumption. Weight Watchers is an effective program that helps people to become more aware of how many calories are consumed. Simply writing down the foods eaten throughout the day can increase awareness and decrease food consumption.

Know How Many Hours of Sleep You Get Nightly

Seven to eight hours of sleep a night is recommended. Researchers suggest that people sleeping less than six hours of sleep nightly have lower overall blood flow to the brain. Decreasing blood flow to the brain also limits oxygen flow to the brain, which can lead to cognitive decline.

Know Your Blood Pressure

High blood pressure is associated with lower overall brain function, in great part due to limiting blood flow to the brain. Blood pressure readings include the following:
- Optimal to normal blood pressure: 120/80 mm/Hg and below
- Hypertension or high blood pressure: 140/90 mm/Hg and above

Know Your Lipid Panel

Approximately 60 percent of the brain's solid weight is fat. It is important to have a healthy amount of fat in the body and the brain. The American Heart Association recommendations are as follows:
- Total cholesterol (<200mg/dL)
- HDL (>60mg/dL)
- LDL (<100mg/dL)
- Triglycerides (100mg/dL)

#55: Develop new talents. Knit, paint, or learn a new sport to challenge your brain and body to work together in new ways.

Engagement in meaningful activities that require active new learning will develop new connections in your brain. You will activate neurons in the brain, build new brain cells, and develop new synaptical connections as the neurons fire and wire together because of the new activities.

Try something you've always thought about doing, but never had or taken the time to do. Learn a new language, take a cooking class, learn to sketch or draw, or join a choir. So many opportunities are available to engage in new learning experiences to get you out of your box and stimulate the brain to grow.

Challenge your body by using your nondominant hand to eat a meal. Close one eye as you walk through your home. Listen to part of movie without watching, as you sit on a stability ball. That will challenge your brain to create a visual of the movie while engaging your core to maintain a neutral spine to sit comfortably.

Take advantage of one of many educational opportunities by enrolling in classes or workshops offered through local adult education programs, community college, or university. Try a bible study at a local church to engage with new people and gain new perspectives.

It's easy to get in a box and do the same things, keep the same routine, and spend time with the same people. Step outside of your box with new engaging activities that will stimulate and grow the brain.

#56: Learn a new word or fact each day to enhance your brain's ability to make new memories.

Exercising the brain in a variety of ways is as important as exercising the body with a cross-training approach. Learning a new word each day expands vocabulary and increases the brain's memory-building power. A new fact a day expands knowledge and stretches memory capabilities.

Whenever the brain encounters a new word, the language centers of the brain in the prefrontal lobe along with working (short-term) and long-term memory is challenged to build new memories in the hippocampus. The brain will build a new network of neurons specifically for remembering the new word. A variety of websites are available to access a new word a day: www.merriam-webster.com/word-of-the-day and www.wordsmith.org/awad are two options. If a book is preferred, a dictionary is a good start.

Learning a new fact and reviewing it to move it from short- to long-term memory gives the brain practice in processing, understanding, and remembering new information to be stored in short-term memory in the hippocampus, where it can be transferred to long-term memory storage. Building new memories stretches the brain's ability to build long-term memory. Many books and websites contain facts. With so much to learn, you can easily engage the brain with new and interesting facts.

iStockphoto/Thinkstock

#57: Take a different route to a usual destination to take your brain off autopilot; new directions make new connections.

The principle of adaptation refers to the body getting used to exercise or training after repeated exposure to it. In order to improve the physical fitness components of cardiovascular endurance or muscle strength, endurance, and flexibility, progressive overload is required. Progressive overload is the gradual increase of stress placed on the body during exercise. The brain responds in much the same way. A pattern of avoiding new situations, experiences, and learning opportunities leads to a decrease in mental performance in older years.

If you have ever moved to a new neighborhood in the same community, changed offices at work, or moved things at home or work to a different spot, you have probably also caught yourself going to the old place out of habit. One simple way to take the brain off autopilot and get it working to make new connections is to take a different route to a usual destination. It is a simple way to cross-train the brain. The following simple activities can get the brain off autopilot to make new connections with a different direction:

- Take a different route to the grocery store or work.
- Move silverware to a different drawer.
- Eat dinner backwards, starting with dessert.
- Change the order of an exercise routine.
- Rearrange furniture in your home or work.
- Take a walk in a different area.
- Start grocery shopping in a different aisle of the store.
- Eat breakfast at dinnertime.
- Sit in a different place to eat dinner.
- Change the organization of a clothing closet.

#58: Play board, card, or computer games with friends and on your own to improve your ability to concentrate, while boosting neuronal growth with new activities.

The *New England Journal of Medicine* reported that adults who engage in stimulating mental activities are 63 percent less likely to develop dementia than those who don't. Playing games, especially with others, boosts neuronal growth by challenging the brain to process new rules, strategies, and information to play the game. Playing games with others improves cooperation skills as well as ability to work with others to achieve a goal.

Many board games provide real mental challenge. Chess has been found to strengthen skills in math, reading, reasoning abilities, memory, and logic. Backgammon, monopoly, scrabble, checkers, and even aggravation challenge the brain to remember rules, strategize, and apply the rules and strategies.

Computer and video games are often the target of criticism, but research suggests that benefits (like improving processing speed) are associated with playing these games. Computer and video games may also increase response time and attention to detail. Computer and video game play may also improve visual-spatial capacity, the ability to multi-task, make decisions, and track objects. By challenging many areas of the brain to respond together, a boost in neuronal growth results.

Goodshoot

#59: Socialize to decrease loneliness, depression, and stress while boosting brain connections. Socialization is a critical domain of a brain-healthy lifestyle.

A positive relationship can be found between social engagement and cognitive performance. Animal researches found that the size of an animal's brain correlated with the size of social groups they formed. It is believed that the same is true for people.

Researchers analyzed data of 1,667 adults who were 60 years and older over several years. Participants engaging in social activities with friends and family, joining clubs, and going to social engagements had better cognitive ability and better memory compared to people who socialized less. Older adults who were less socially active than those who were socially active had both cognitive and physical limitations. The results are stunning; the socially active group had healthier brain scans and better physical health. The type of social engagement plays a role as well. Those people engaged in high levels of communication while socializing perform better on cognitive tests than those watching TV with others.

Chronic isolation can lead to depression. Those people with more social interaction are less likely to experience chronic depression. Socialization also decreases feelings of loneliness and lowers stress. Older adults who stay connected socially are more likely to retain their memories and cognitive abilities later in life.

The take-home message from a recently published study in the *Journal of Health and Social Behavior* is that people need a variety of kinds of brain stimulation, including social activity, to keep their minds sharp. This is especially true later in life, when aging takes its toll on memory and other complex neurological processes.

#60: Volunteer to connect with others, boost self-confidence, and increase life satisfaction.

Volunteering is a meaningful way to stay in contact with people while doing good things to help others. The social connection and the do-good experience releases feel good endorphins in the brain to boost self-confidence and improve life satisfaction. Volunteering engages the mind and body and can reduce risk of health-related diseases like dementia and Alzheimer's.

So many opportunities to volunteer and make a difference in the lives of others and in your community are available. Think about your skills, talents, and interests, and then consider whom they can benefit. Tutoring a student, serving meals to homebound elderly, building or repairing flooded homes, singing in an assisted living facility, or joining a fundraising effort to help those in need are a few ways you can help others and in turn reap personal benefits.

Top Five Reasons to Volunteer

- Helping others boosts endorphins, the feel-good hormones.
- Volunteering focuses the mind on helping others which lowers cortisol, the stress hormone.
- The satisfaction of helping others increases self-worth, self-confidence, and life satisfaction.
- Volunteer experiences create new networks of friends and open the mind to new perspectives.
- Staying engaged and involved in a variety of activities engages the mind to learn new things, developing new brain connections.

#61: Join clubs and recreational groups to develop new friendships, learn different things, stay active, and keep the brain engaged.

Socialization is key to a healthy brain. Getting involved in clubs and recreational groups is a great way to develop friendships with people who have similar interests. For example, a person interested in tennis, bowling, golf, or basketball can join a league to meet people who enjoy the same kind of sport activity. Fitness centers and YMCAs often have rec leagues. Most communities have a city recreation program that has a wide variety of sport activities, especially for young people. School activities can provide an introduction to becoming involved in sport activities. Friendship and activity are both good for the brain.

Someone interested in cooking can learn more about cooking and get new recipes while cultivating new friendships. A quilting club is an opportunity to strengthen hands and fingers while bonding with new people, and the end project may be a keepsake for life.

Service clubs provide a great opportunity to network with others while building friendships and professional relationships. Rotary, Kiwanis, and Sertoma are some of the well-recognized service clubs. Each service club has a different mission and offers an opportunity to help others. Guest speakers often provide education for service club meetings, which adds yet another opportunity to learn and grow.

Encouraging club involvement in young people while attending kindergarten through 12th grade can provide a good foundation for getting involved. Communities offer information regarding clubs and organizations on public library websites. An online search can also provide good information to help select a club or recreational opportunity.

#62: Attend a conference. It is a great way to strengthen what you know and learn new things while developing new relationships.

Conferences offer a variety of opportunities to learn new concepts and develop new skills and techniques through lectures, workshops that have a more hands-on activity focus, panel discussions, poster presentations, and other session formats. A person can maximize conference time by reviewing the conference session overviews to select those that have the most personal and professional value. Most conferences offer session outlines online for attendees to download for a print copy or for taking notes electronically.

It is important to review what has been learned at the conference to begin to commit information to memory. One of the best ways to anchor learning of the conference material is to teach what has been learned to others.

The conversations that take place between sessions and at networking events during the conference provide valuable exchanges that can expand perspectives on sessions and generate new ideas from the experiences shared by colleagues. If a person is attending a conference with a group, it is beneficial for individuals to attend different sessions and then discuss information at the end of the day. If the group attends all of the same sessions, different perspectives can be shared, but often less networking with new people results.

Presenting at the conference can take the experience to another level. A person learns best what he teaches, so preparing a session for presentation is a valuable brain booster. The conference presenters often have an opportunity to meet with each other to create a new network of professional connections. Conferences often need volunteers to help with registration, introduction of speakers, and monitoring sessions. This is a good way to see the behind-the-scenes activity of the conference.

Professional organizations and associations are a good resource for learning more about business-related conferences. Personal growth conferences may include a women's wellness weekend or a couples' retreat. An online search is a good start to finding a conference of interest for those wanting to increase lifelong learning.

#63: Learn a second language.

Research suggests that fluency in more than one language may have a positive effect on memory performance and problem-solving abilities. One study suggested that students who studied a second language in schools scored higher on verbal and math abilities on the SAT. Another study found that the brain density of bilingual people is greater than that of the brains of people who are monolingual. The thickness was most prevalent in the left hemisphere in the language areas of the brain (Wernicke's and Broca's area). Learning a second language is a good mental workout for the brain. Speaking two languages can cause physical changes in the brain that result in better cognition and brain health.

Taking a foreign language class is one of the best ways to learn a new language. Practicing the language in conversation is key to becoming proficient. Visiting a foreign country that speaks the language can effectively challenge the brain to interpret and speak the language. Many self-learning tools are available; Rosetta Stone is one of the most popular.

iStockphoto/Thinkstock

#64: Ask questions and listen; practice Stephen Covey's "Seek first to understand, then to be understood" to achieve empathetic listening and boost memory.

In Stephen Covey's book, *The 7 Habits of Highly Effective People*®, the fifth habit is "Seek first to understand, then to be understood." This kind of empathetic listening can serve as a brain booster in three ways. Empathetic listening trains the brain to listen with focus, search for meaning without allowing personal opinions or beliefs to interpret information, and achieve mutual consensus when problem solving and making decisions.

Effective communication is one of the most important abilities in life. Listening is one of the most important skills of effective communication. Most people listen with intent to reply; as the other person talks, a typical listener is formulating what he is going to say. The four levels of listening include: ignoring, pretending, selective listening, and attentive listening. Seeking first to understand is the practice of attentive listening taken to the next level. Attending to what is said to truly understand is empathetic listening—listening with focus, not allowing outside or internal distractions to interrupt the message of the person talking.

Keeping the focus on the speaker's message will allow the listener to clearly hear the message without placing personal perspective on the information. This requires focus and the practice of being open-minded.

Empathetic listening also builds trust in relationships. With trusting relationships, problem-solving, decision-making, and personal and professional goals can be achieved.

Training the brain to practice empathetic listening is also skill that can help organize information in the brain to boost the ability to boost and retrieve memories.

#65: Exercise with a friend. It will keep you accountable for your exercise plans and give you something to look forward to doing.

A person's success in sticking to an exercise program increases when exercising with a friend. Exercising with a friend keeps a person more accountable. It is easy to skip an exercise session when exercising alone. A person is less likely to skip a buddy exercise session, as it is an appointment with another person. A person is also more likely to work harder with the encouragement of someone committed to the same activity. Exercising with a friend can also be an excellent way to socialize while burning calories.

Tips for a Positive and Successful Exercise Friend Relationship

- Choose an exercise friend who is good company, committed, and motivated.
- Find an exercise buddy who has a similar schedule and common exercise interests.
- If possible, select an exercise friend with comparable skill and fitness level.
- Stick to the planned activity, and avoid the alternative of "going for lunch."
- Have fun and enjoy, challenging each other with new activities and intensity levels.

Stockbyte

#66: Keep a "grateful journal" by writing down at least one good thing that happened in your day, which helps to train your brain to make positive memories.

Thoughts are powerful. A person thinks approximately 50,000 thoughts a day. What a person thinks is personal reality. A person owns the physiology of each thought. Positive thoughts lower the stress hormone cortisol and lead to positive brain and body health. Negative thoughts increase the stress hormone cortisol and have a negative impact on the health of the brain and body.

Negative thoughts can lead to worry, depression, anxiety, fear, unhappiness, and decreased motivation. Studies show that rumination, continual worry, and negative thinking patterns decrease functioning in the frontal lobe of the brain. Negative attitudes can easily spread to others.

A grateful journal can be personalized in any way. It may have three key focuses a day, like stating:

- I am grateful for _____.
- I am good at _____.
- One thing I did for someone else today was _____.

Positive thoughts lead to happiness, productivity, strong problem-solving skills, and better brain function. A grateful journal is an opportunity to focus on the good things in life. The journal can identify good things that happened during the day, list something a person is grateful for in their day or life, and include good things done for others to raise awareness while increasing acts of service and kindness. What you think about, you bring about. A grateful journal is a good way to reinforce positive thinking and create positive memories.

Your beliefs become your thoughts,
Your thoughts become your words,
Your words become your actions,
Your actions become your habits,
Your habits become your values,
Your values become your destiny.
– Mohandas Karamchand Gandhi

#67: Meditate to make stronger connections between brain regions and experience less brain atrophy.

Meditation practices have various health benefits, including the possibility of preserving cognition and preventing dementia. Meditation increases levels of brain-derived neurotrophic factor, boosting memory and brain growth. Meditation also reduces stress and feelings of fatigue by reducing the stress hormone cortisol. Meditation enhances positive emotions and increases sense of well-being and joy.

Within the growing field of study called contemplative neuroscience, the brain science of meditation, neuroscientists are seeing that just as specific exercises can strengthen a target muscle, activities like meditation can strengthen areas of the brain.

Researchers have discovered that people who meditate regularly for many years have increased thickness in critical brain regions associated with attention and sensory processing. Studies indicate that the meditative practice of focusing attention on your breath or a mantra helps the brain restructure itself to make concentration easier. The practice of calm acceptance during meditation will develop a brain that is more resilient to stress.

Key Benefits of Meditation

- Increase brain volume.
- Improve concentration.
- Reduce stress and improve health.
- Enhance knowledge of self.

The number-one excuse for not meditating (like the number-one excuse for not exercising) is "not enough time." Like anything worthwhile, quality meditation does take patience and time.

Tips for Meditation

- Sit in good posture in a quiet place.
- Focus the mind in the present.
- Pay attention to the breath.
- Gently release thoughts and focus on the breath.
- Start with 5 to 10 minutes and gradually increase meditation time.
- Enjoy.

#68: Think about what you are thinking to take control of your thoughts, enhance cognitive flexibility, and strengthen your ability to know and govern yourself.

Researchers suggest that the human mind thinks 50,000 to 60,000 thoughts a day. Each thought can affect the physiology of the body. A positive thought can help balance good hormones in the body. A positive thought is uplifting and affects the person and those around him in positive ways.

A negative thought stimulates a release of the stress hormone cortisol. A negative thought can cause the brain's emotional center, the amygdala, to overreact and cut off the transmission of information to the frontal lobe of the brain, where reasoning and decision-making takes place. An overactive amygdala can influence bad decision making, which, like a domino effect, can create more problems.

The type of thinking you choose will become automatic over time. Depression, anxiety, and low self-esteem are often the result of feeding the brain with negative thoughts. The negative thoughts become a pattern of thinking that leads to a negative outcome. Dr. Daniel Amen refers to automatic negative thoughts as ANTs that need to be stomped out. When a negative thought enters the mind, be aware of that thought, and counter it with a positive thought and stomp out the ANT.

The message is to choose thoughts wisely, as thoughts become actions, actions become habits, and habits become character traits. Each person has control of three things: what the person thinks, says, and does. Pay attention to thoughts and choose positive thinking patterns.

#69: Practice mindfulness by focusing on what is happening around you without judgment to reduce stress, depression, and anxiety.

Mindfulness is the conscious practice of taking information from your surroundings and situations with an open mind. The mind is like a parachute; it works best when it is open. The world is seen through the filters of experience, beliefs, and attitudes. Becoming open to new information and new points of view is an important feature of mindfulness.

Mindfulness is a process, which encourages the perspective that life is a process and not an outcome. For example, it is not just the score of the game that is the focus, but how the players arrived at that score. Mindfulness sometimes may mean taking "The Why Test," to help determine why you do the things you do. The process of open-mindedly thinking through the why can help a person realize that it was done because that is the way it has always been done and it may have been for reasons that are no longer valid.

Mindfulness on aging is stepping out of the thinking that an age determines what you should think, do, wear, eat, or live. Aging mindfully is the choice to consider possibilities and believe in abilities in an open-minded way for healthy aging to occur. Consider the question, "If you didn't know how old you were, how old would you think you are?"

Mindfulness is looking outside of the box to solve problems and identify new solutions. It is practicing Stephen Covey's principle of empathetic listening, "Seek first to understand, then to be understood." Mindfulness is the practice of not taking things personally, but rather observing what is happening without thinking that is happening to you.

Mindfulness is a practice that can help the brain's limbic system process thoughts in a healthy way to reduce reacting and increase responding with a more clear understanding of the big picture. Mindfulness can reduce the levels of stress hormones in the body and decrease life conflict.

#70: Use your nondominant side more often to create pathways across your left- and right-brain hemispheres.

The brain continuously changes through the growth of new neurons and new neuronal pathways. Using your nondominant hand will challenge your brain to adapt to the new movement. When the dominant hand is used, one hemisphere of the brain is activated. When using the nondominant hand, both brain hemispheres work so that movement can happen more efficiently. Challenge your brain by using your nondominant hand to brush your teeth, comb your hair, button a shirt, zip your pants, write, open the door, wash your body, butter toast, wave to a friend, dribble a basketball, throw a ball, or open a jar. The more the nondominant hand is used, the more the left and right hemispheres of the brain will work together to create pathways for efficient movement while improving brain and motor function.

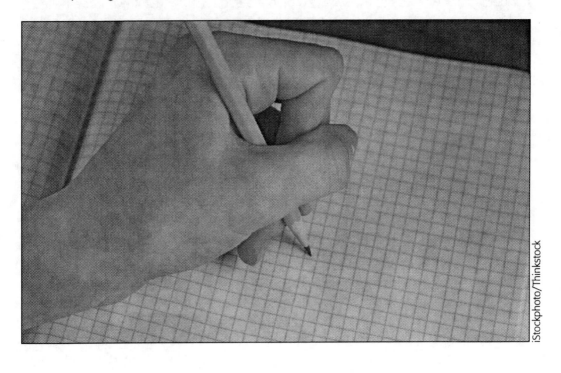

iStockphoto/Thinkstock

#71: Take brain breaks because a person's attention span is 8 to 20 minutes, depending on age and interest in the subject matter.

The brain learns best when it is engaged in learning, like when things are novel or the topic or subject matter is interesting. Even when the learner is engaged, the brain tends to downshift after 8 to 20 minutes. It is helpful to take a break to allow the brain to absorb what it is learning, doing, or experiencing and give it necessary time to be ready to refocus. Brain breaks can also get blood flowing and get necessary oxygen and fluids to the brain.

For example, during a 50-minute class time, the learner will remember best what is learned first, second best what is learned last, and third best what is in the middle. If there is a brain break after 20 minutes, it will help the brain to absorb and remember better. If the brain break is an activity that uses the information learned in the first 20 minutes it will help in processing and remembering the information.

A brain break that is movement-oriented is also very effective. A short walk is a good brain break. Standing up and going to get a drink of water or a healthy snack incorporates movement with providing fluids or nutrients the brain needs. Marching in place or seated in a chair is another option. A seated stretch walking hands down to the ankles and coming back up to a seated position will stretch muscles and increase blood flow. Sitting up straight and tall while engaging the abdominal muscles as shoulders are lifted and rolled up and back will help the body get back in good posture while giving the brain a break. Sitting up straight and tall, reaching the hands behind the back and grasping the opposite elbow while looking over one shoulder and then the other gives the brain and the back a break. Practicing the breathing exercises in #29 or the cross-lateral movements in #73 are more brain break options. Move, breathe and hydrate to give the brain a boost and increase ability to pay attention.

#72: Engage in chair marching to move the large muscles of your body to increase blood and oxygen flow to the brain.

Humans are professional sitters. Much of work and leisure time is spent sitting. A person can increase flow of blood and oxygen to the brain without even leaving the chair. Marching while seated in a chair is a simple way to feed the brain with necessary oxygen and nutrients by increasing muscle contraction and boosting metabolism.

Begin chair marching by sitting up straight and tall with shoulders stacked over the hips. Contract the abdominal muscles to keep the spine in neutral. March the feet, lifting the feet and knees as high as comfortable. Vary the speed of the marching, starting slowly and gradually increasing speed and intensity. March the feet close together and then wide. March one foot out to the side and back to center. March the opposite foot out to the side and back to center. March feet close together and gradually march them as wide apart as comfortable. Vary the marching by adding knee lifts. For example, march eight times, and then do four knee lifts; march 16 times, and then do eight knee lifts.

Music can help to set the pace of chair marching while boosting energy and lifting mood. Marching while seated in a chair is a simple way to fit fitness into the work day and implement an energy boost into the popular leisure time activity of watching TV. March, march, march; movement in a seated position makes sitting less hazardous to the health!

#73: Perform seated or standing cross-lateral movement to strengthen the corpus callosum, the part of the brain that connects right and left hemispheres.

The corpus callosum is a thick band of nerve fibers that both divide and connect the left and right hemispheres of the brain. The left side of the brain controls the right side of the body, and the right side of the brain controls the left side of the body. The two sides of the brain are forced to communicate when the arm or leg crosses the midline of the body. Cross-lateral movement strengthens and builds the neuronal connections between the right and left hemispheres.

Sports like tennis, golf, soccer, basketball, and badminton that involve crossing the arm or leg to the opposite side of the body are among the activities that are excellent for strengthening the corpus callosum. Following are a few other examples of cross-lateral exercises:

- Reach the right hand over your body, and tap your left knee. Repeat with the opposite side.
- Touch the right ear with the left hand. Repeat in reverse.
- Do the same activities standing or marching.
- Play the game Twister®.

Books with cross-lateral movement ideas include:
- *Start Smart* by Pam Schiller
- *Brain Gym* by Paul and Gail Dennison
- *Sensorcises* by Laurie Glazener

#74: Energize with chair dancing to a wide variety of music, and stimulate your brain and body to move to varied rhythm patterns.

Music can lift mood and elevate energy level. Dancing elevates levels of endorphins and in the brain to improve mood. Dancing lowers stress by decreasing the stress hormone cortisol. Dancing engages the temporal lobe of the brain, where auditory processing occurs. Dancing requires the cerebellum and the motor cortex (located in the posterior area of the frontal lobe of the brain) to work together to coordinate movement and rhythm patterns. Dancing increases heart rate and respiration, which increases blood flow to the brain. Dancing while seated in a chair in a classroom, at home, in a workplace, or in a meeting when people have become disengaged is a convenient and effective way to stimulate and energize the brain and body.

Researchers have found that dancing can be as effective in treating depression as antidepressants like Zoloft®. Dancing can reduce risk of Alzheimer's by over 50 percent. Dancing is one of the best activities for longevity. If a person doesn't have the space, a partner, or time for 20 minutes of dancing, incorporate a 60-second or one song chair dance into the day to improve brain and body health. Choose favorite tunes and freestyle dance, or challenge the brain with some new choreography. The following sections offer a few energizing chair dance examples.

Hip-Hop Chair (Music: "1, 2 Step" by Ciara)

- 4 count shoulder rock
- 4 count double-arm circle
- 4 count shoulder brush 3, shoulder roll-out
- 4 count shoulder rolls back
- 8 count opposite corner arms
- 4 count legs step out and in
- 4 count heel lift

Simple Waltz Line Dance in Chair (Music: "Open Arms" by Journey)

- Four forward back waltz steps
- Four side-to-side waltz steps
- Upper body: Imaginary partner closed position, sway side, push forward/pull back
- Conduct the band in 3/4 time with the arms.
- Add toe taps or heel lifts.

Polka in Chair (Music: "Beer Barrel Polka")

- March 3, heel
- March 3, kick
- March 3, knee
- Knee lifts 4 times with the right and then the left, 2 times with the right and then the left, 1 time with the right and then the left; clap the same-side hand on the leg to challenge the brain more.

iStockphoto/Thinkstock

#75: Give the brain time to process and learn.

The hippocampus is a small crescent-shaped structure in the temporal lobe where short-term or working memory is stored. This area has a small memory capacity. The hippocampus organizes, sorts, and processes new information or working memory before it is sent out to various parts of the brain where it is stored in long-term memory. The brain cannot continuously learn an unlimited amount of new content. In order for information to move to long-term memory, processing time is needed.

Learners will process information better and more quickly if they already have an understanding of the subject. It's important for teachers to keep in mind that it is not as important to simply cover a certain amount of material, but for students to learn it. Self-learning carries the same principle: become familiar with the content and vocabulary of what is to be learned, and then build on the knowledge. Applying new knowledge is key to converting it to long-term memory.

The organization of the content of a lesson, sermon, or presentation can help to boost learning. An effective and simple format is: tell them what you are going to tell them, tell them, then tell them what you told them. That is a very simplified version of lesson design, which begins with an anticipatory set and introduction to get learners ready for what is to come, instruction followed by guided and independent practice, and closure or a review of what was learned.

When learning is well-organized, the brain will process information and store it more effectively. The learner will also be challenged to learn, but not stressed in a way that can be harmful to the brain and body. If there is too much information and learning, it becomes a threat, and the associated stress will impair learning. That stress also increases levels of the stress hormone cortisol, which can be harmful to the brain and body. Giving the brain time to process and learn can increase learning and boost brain function.

#76: Eat from the four food groups.

Proteins found in meat, legumes, and tofu can provide increased alertness and help stabilize memory because proteins contain the amino acid L-tyrosine that produces norepinephrine and dopamine. Proteins contain the amino acids that are used to make the neurotransmitters used by the brain for communication and networking. Neurotransmitters help the brain focus and shift attention, balance mood, and excite or calm the brain.

Fats found in dairy, meat, and oils are crucial for memory formation and the strength of the neuronal membranes. Fats produce acetylcholine, which is a building block of the neuronal membrane and serves as a neurotransmitter, carrying messages in the brain and body. Fatty acids from fats help the brain to think and feel. Approximately 60 percent of brain matter consists of fats that create the cell membranes of the body.

Carbohydrates provide the glucose the brain needs for energy. Complex carbohydrates provide glucose for longer periods, and simple carbohydrates provide a quick energy boost. Some foods considered as sources of simple carbohydrates (sugars) include fruits, sweets, baked goods, and soda. Whole grains, breads, oats, and brown rice are complex carbohydrates.

Complex carbohydrates found in vegetables, grains, and fruits provide a sense of satiety (fullness) and relaxation largely from the high levels of L-tryptophan, which produces serotonin, the policeman of the brain that can help the brain stay focused.

Dairy products also play a role in brain health. Adults consuming dairy products five to six times a week performed better on memory tests than those not consuming dairy products.

#77: Stand up and sit down to fit fitness into your life and energize your brain while doing one of the top five exercises for lower body: a squat.

Recent surveys show that, worldwide, people spend about 300 minutes, 20 percent of their day, sitting. One study suggested people spend approximately 50 to 70 percent of wake time sitting. Research indicates that sitting for more than three hours a day can decrease life expectancy by two years. Long periods of sitting affect the entire body in a negative way. While sitting, blood pools in the legs, and the brain doesn't get much-needed blood, which delivers oxygen and nutrients to the brain. Too much sitting increases risk of premature death, causes obesity, affects cholesterol levels, and increases risk of heart disease and diabetes. In a seated position, muscles don't contract and, therefore, require less fuel—so stand up and sit down.

One of the number-one excuses for not exercising is "I don't have time." A great way for you to fit fitness into your life and energize your brain is to stand up and sit down, stand up and sit down, and repeat that movement until the muscles are tired. To challenge the muscles even more, hold the hips a few inches above the chair with the knees over the ankles and the core muscles engaged; that's a squat and one of the top five exercises for the lower body.

iStockphoto/Thinkstock

#78: Whirl and twirl and spin and turn around to stimulate alertness and attention, and to improve reading skills.

Merry-go-rounds and some swings have been removed from parks and playgrounds due to increased liability insurance costs. The spinning and swinging motion that is associated with activities on this equipment is some of the best movement to stimulate the inner ear system (vestibular system). Spinning, whirling, and twirling lead to alertness, attention, and improvement in reading skills. These movements are great for developing the brain and keeping the vestibular system healthy.

The vestibular system helps to maintain stationary and movement orientation. It works closely with the cerebellum to keep the body in balance. Three semicircular canals in the inner ear are filled with fluid. Any movement sets the fluid in motion. Children with vestibular problems demonstrate delays in motor development, balance, language development, reading, and writing.

It's easy to exercise the vestibular system; just stand and reach your arms out to the side and turn around for 5 to 15 seconds. Change the activity by bringing your hands folded across the chest. Spinning with one or both eyes closed will add even more of a challenge to the vestibular system. This activity is a great brain break in the classroom or office.

Take a dance class. Play with your children and grandchildren; create a twirling game for them that releases extra energy and develops the vestibular system at the same time. Whirling, twirling, and spinning are movements that make a difference in the brain.

#79: Sit on a stability ball to improve focus and ability to stay on task; engaging the body engages the brain.

Stability balls (or balance balls) were designed in the 1960s as a physical therapy tool. Stability balls are a functional training tool used in group exercise, personal training, at home, and in the gym. Stability balls are now being used in schools, offices, and at home as a chair to improve posture, increase abdominal and back strength, and increase focus.

One study showed that students with ADHD improved behavior and the ability to write words legibly. Students were able to sit still, focus, and write words more clearly. Sitting on a stability ball requires physical energy to keep the ball stable and can increase ability to concentrate. When a person sits on a stability ball, both sides of the brain are engaged in keeping the body centered on the ball. When the brain is stimulated, it is more focused on learning. Teachers have also reported an increase in attention, desk work, and reading.

Stability balls can be purchased at sporting goods stores or department stores. They can also be purchased online at a variety of sites, including www.gaiam.com/Balance_ Balls *or* www.spri.com. It is important to select a stability ball that is the correct size. Many size charts are available; the following is a general guideline for ball size selection.

Height	Ball Size
Less than 5'0"	45 cm (18 inches)
5'0" to 5'5"	55 cm (22 inches)
5'6" to 6'1"	65 cm (26 inches)
6'2" to 6'8"	75 cm (30 inches)
6'9" and up	85 cm (34 inches)

#80: Do a walking review on your own or with someone; say things you are learning out loud while moving, so that the brain is getting oxygen-rich blood while rehearsing.

It is estimated that a person remembers only 10 percent of what is read and only 5 percent of what is heard. A person remembers as much as 90 percent of information he personally teaches to others. A walking review can provide a person the opportunity to teach another person what is learned, increasing retention of information while increasing blood flow to the brain. Repeating information out loud helps to anchor learning. Rehearsal helps to ensure information is remembered. Walking while doing a review talk boosts the brain with oxygenated blood while repeating to remember.

Jupiterimages

#81: Go outside and get sunshine and fresh air to reduce depression, regulate melatonin (the sleep hormone), and lower levels of cortisol (the stress hormone).

Outdoor light and fresh air can increase alertness and attention, boosting productivity and learning, while reducing depression. Lack of outdoor light will have the opposite effect, increasing levels of depression and decreasing alertness, leading to lower levels of productivity and learning. Over the past century, the amount of outdoor light individuals are exposed to has declined significantly. Ultraviolet lighting found in most schools and workplaces absorbs essential minerals, like calcium, that can reduce ability to think clearly. Limited outdoor light and fresh air may also have a negative effect on health and is associated with depression.

Research suggests that students with the most daylight in classrooms make better school progress. Brighter indoor lighting and maximizing outdoor lighting can improve visual difficulties, decrease fatigue, improve posture, and decrease sickness. Brighter light makes for better visual acuity and less eye strain. Insufficient light sends a message to the brain that it's time to be drowsy or worried, triggering sleep or the release of the stress hormone cortisol. Increased outside light and fresh air will have the opposite affect, increasing energy and ability to focus while decreasing feelings of stress (lowering cortisol levels). Outside light also helps to regulate the body's levels of melatonin (sleep hormone) so that the body is wakeful during the day and ready for sleep at night.

Stockbyte

#82: Be a lifelong learner to keep your brain active and growing.

A long-term aging study discovered the three factors shared by people with the least cognitive decline: education, self-efficacy, and exercise. Study after study shows that the more education a person has, the higher the cognitive (thinking) abilities and the lower the incidence of dementia.

The body can develop muscle and new neurons and neuronal connections at any age. The ability of the brain to change is known as brain plasticity or neuroplasticity. The brain is plastic and can grow and change through adulthood. Neurogenesis occurs with new learning at any age and stage of life. Lifelong learning occurs not only in a classroom, but by engaging in new learning experiences, doing new and different things, stimulating the brain with new sensations, and engaging in varied opportunities. The use-it-or-lose-it principle of exercise to fitness also applies to brain growth and cognitive functioning. Learning new things exercises the brain. Brain fitness throughout the lifespan is an important of successful and happy aging.

iStockphoto/Thinkstock

#83: Pay attention. The intention to focus leads to retention of information.

The brain is bombarded with sights, sounds, smells, and touch. All of the sensory stimuli coming at the brain can be overwhelming, so the brain focuses on what it deems important. The brain is wired for survival. If the brain hears a loud noise, attention is focused quickly to the sound to check for a possible threat. If a person hasn't eaten and is hungry, that is where the brain's attention is focused. It is estimated that 1 percent of daily messages in the form of information, sights, sounds, and feelings are going to have people's awareness. The others will disappear. It is a matter of what the brain thinks is important and, therefore, really up to an individual to make an effort to pay attention.

It is important to notice with intent. If a person intends to focus on learning people's names and focuses attention on the name and the face, repeating the name verbally and in thought, that name has a better chance of being remembered. If the brain is made aware of key points, it needs to know and intends to listen, look for, and remember those key points, it is more likely to remember.

An instructive tale is that of a good preacher who always had a full house at Sunday services. When asked to share points on how to keep a congregation engaged, the preacher said that sermons were 10 minutes in length, keeping within limits of attention span. The preacher also shared, "I tell them what I am going to tell them, I tell them, and I tell them what I told them." If the brain knows what it needs to focus on, focuses on it, and does a review for closure, with intention will be retention.

#84: Engage in rehearsal/overlearn because information remains in short-term memory for only 15 to 20 seconds unless you anchor the learning in meaningful ways.

Sensory memory involves input from vision (reading), hearing (listening to a lecture), touch (dribbling a basketball), and other senses. Those sensations last only briefly, unless the brain is directed to pay attention. If focus is on the incoming information, it will be transitioned to working memory. It's working memory that starts to make sense of and use the information. Using the information that is in working memory by practicing something new, reviewing information, talking about what is learned, or writing notes is a good beginning to moving information into long-term memory storage. The transfer process can take up to 24 hours, and in cases where information is complex, it may require practice and rehearsal over a long period of time. Sleep is important in the process of transferring information from working memory to long-term memory.

Tips to Anchor Learning

- Write things down.
- Rehearse what has been learned by repeating it silently or out loud.
- Teach what has been learned to others.
- Apply knowledge in meaningful ways.
- Get a good night's sleep.

#85: Develop the three memory pathways—semantic (meaning), episodic (stories), and procedural (how to)—in order to retain and retrieve memory.

Memory is a mental process of storage and retrieval of information and experience. Information enters memory through senses. It is then processed by multiple memory systems in the brain and stored for later use

Semantic memory is the general information that is stored in long-term memory that is not linked to time or place. It is related to who, what, and why.

Episodic memory is associated with time and place, where information is experienced or learned. Episodic memory remembers where and when. It helps to remember a person at a salad bar in the cafeteria at noon on Monday.

Procedural memory stores information on how to do something. Procedural memory holds knowledge about skills and habits. It can happen that a person with brain trauma has difficulty remembering people or situations, but can remember how to do puzzles or play cards.

The more memory systems are engaged in storing and retrieving information, the higher the chance of retrieval. Memories are stored in different areas of the brain, like information is stored in different files in a computer. Episodic and procedural memory can be useful in recall. In order for a person access to something from memory storage, it may be helpful to think through what occurred during that time frame. What else happened that day? What were you wearing? Who were you with? What were you doing? Although these questions represent different memory systems, they are interconnected. Thinking about the desired memory from alternative perspectives can help to activate other related memory systems that are linked to that memory. This, in turn, will activate the system that holds the memory that a person wishes to recall. Who, what, when, where, why, and how are keys to storing and retrieving memory.

#86: Use all learning modalities. Link visual, auditory, and kinesthetic activity in the learning process to strengthen connections in the brain.

Learners use all three styles—visual, auditory, and kinesthetic—to receive and learn new information and experiences. One or two of these styles is usually dominant, the best way a person learns. The style of learning may also be different for different tasks.

Visual learners like to learn through written language, such as reading and writing tasks. Visual learners use outlines, handouts, charts, visual illustrations, slide presentations, and information in text. Visual learners are more likely to take notes and are more likely to remember what they write down. Visual learners like to see what they are learning and often close their eyes to visualize and remember something. They tend to sit in the front.

Auditory learners remember better what is heard. Auditory learners benefit from listening to lectures, participating in talking activities like group jigsaw (where individuals discuss information within a group), playing games like Jeopardy!, verbalizing questions, and teaching others what they have learned. Auditory learners often talk to themselves, repeating what is learned. They typically move lips when reading and often read out loud to acquire knowledge. They tend to sit where they can hear.

Kinesthetic learners do best when touching (tactile information) and moving (kinesthetic information). Kinesthetic learners take notes and underline and highlight when reading. Kinesthetic learners function best when movement and activity is associated with the learning moment. Kinesthetic learners tend to be active and take frequent breaks. They learn best from hands-on learning activities and learn best from doing.

The more ways people engage visual, auditory, and kinesthetic learning activities, the more they strengthen and make connections in the brain to better remember the material. Strengthening connections between the lobes of the brain where auditory, visual, and kinesthetic information is processed will make the brain more efficient to facilitate learning. Seeing, hearing, and doing can make learning happen.

#87: Tap into multiple intelligences to engage a variety of learning styles; learn through your strengths to improve your weaknesses.

Gardner's theory of multiple intelligences suggests a wide range of cognitive abilities, many ways of being smart. The five intelligences include the following:

- *Logical-mathematical intelligence* is the ability to work better with logic, abstractions, reasoning and numbers, and critical thinking.
- *Visual-spatial intelligence* refers to the ability to see things with the mind's eye and have keen spatial judgment. These people like to draw, read maps, charts, graphs, and daydream.
- People with *high verbal-linguistic intelligence* are good with words and language. They have strong verbal abilities and are good at reading, writing, and telling stories.
- *Bodily-kinesthetic intelligence* is the ability to do well in activities and learning that require muscular movement. These people have good control over body movement and ability to handle objects; they have good eye-hand coordination. Bodily-kinesthetic learners are good at sports, dance, acting, and making things.
- People with *musical intelligence* have special sensitivity to sounds, tones, rhythms, melody, and music. They are able to sing, play musical instruments, and compose music. They tend to be auditory learners.
- High *interpersonal intelligence* refers to the ability to have sensitive to others' moods, feelings, temperaments, and motivations. These people work well in groups and enjoy discussion and debate.
- High *intrapersonal intelligence* refers to the intelligence of understanding self and having the ability to see strengths and weaknesses. This person understands personal unique characteristics and works to develop self.
- *Naturalistic intelligence* is the desire and ability to nurture and relate to one's own environment. This person is interested in plant and animal evolution and classification.

Identify which intelligences are strongest for you by completing a self-assessment. Many assessments are available online. One quick and easy intelligence assessment can be found at www.literacyworks.org/mi/assessment/findyourstrengths.html.

Capitalize on multiple intelligence strengths and develop weaknesses to engage the brain in meaningful ways. Multiple intelligence supports that there are different kinds of smart.

#88: Engage emotions like joy, enthusiasm, and awe to facilitate learning; emotions trigger chemicals that signal the brain "this is important, so keep it."

Emotions trigger chemical changes that alter mood, behavior, and attention. Serotonin and norepinephrine are two neurotransmitters that are closely related to emotion and learning. Serotonin is the policeman of the brain, influencing mood, anger, fear, and self-confidence. Norepinephrine influences attention, perception, and motivation.

The experiences people have generate emotions like fear, anger, surprise, and joy. These emotions generate thoughts, opinions, and decisions. When a person feels confidence, he is more likely to work hard and succeed. When a person approaches a task with optimism, the outcome is more positive. If someone anticipates and looks forward to a learning experience, the brain is more focused than if confusion or frustration is the primary emotion.

The brain is biologically programmed to attend first to information that has strong emotional content. A variety of strategies can provide an emotional hook. Storytelling can be very effective in anchoring learning; it engages the amygdala, the part of the brain that manages emotion. Personalizing information is key to making it meaningful by giving the learner a way to apply content to boost focus. Humor is another way to strengthen memory pathways.

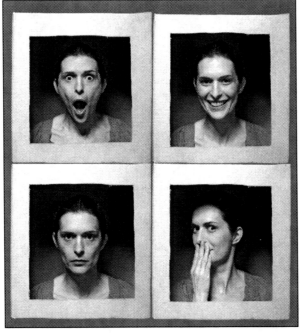

Michael Blann

#89: Reduce learned helplessness by taking control of choices; make a decision to believe you can achieve goals and deal with life challenges in a positive manner.

Learned helplessness is the belief that what you do doesn't matter. Learned helplessness may follow a trauma or threat. It also may stem from consistent experience where there is a lack of control which results in a decision to embrace a "why try" attitude. It could happen if a person just makes a decision that what happens is outside of personal control.

It is key to believe and practice that personal choices greatly affect the health of the brain and body. What a person does, with what he knows, means taking control of choices to make life healthy and productive.

Martin Seligman's approach to learned optimism is an effective exercise in internalizing control. When a person encounters adversity, he reacts by thinking about it. The thoughts are attached to beliefs. The beliefs are the basis of what he thinks and what he does next. By looking at things in a positive way and believing in personal control, the consequence will be more positive than if a person looks at the adversity in a negative way and believes the control is outside of personal control. Research suggests that 50 to 60 percent of disease can be prevented with healthy lifestyle choices. It is also believed that a person has 50 percent control over levels of happiness. Taking control of what a person thinks and what a person does is key to body and brain health and happiness.

#90: Use mnemonics as a way to organize and remember information.

Does the human brain get more forgetful, or does it have more to remember? Does it get harder to remember where things are, or do people have more things to look for? The human brain is fascinating. Retrieving information in the brain is a process that happens at all ages. When a person starts using a new computer that has no information and few programs, it is easy to find things. The longer the person uses the computer and the more programs and information the computer stores, the more challenging it is to remember where to find that information. The same is true of the brain. For example, typically at the age of 25, the brain has significantly fewer names and people to remember than a person does at the age of 50, so is a brain more forgetful, or is it that more file folders (or information stored in the brain) must be sorted through to find the desired information?

Mnemonics provides a system to help the brain organize information. Mnemonics is any information technique that aids information retention. It may be rhyme, a poem, a memorable phrase, or letters from a word that pulls key concepts to mind. Marilee Sprenger's book *Memory 101* uses the acronym N.E.V.E.R. F.O.R.G.E.T. to provide a way to remember key ways to improve memory.

N = Notice.
E = Emote.
V = Visualize.
E = Exercise, and eat right.
R = Rest.

F = Free yourself from stress.
O = Organize.
R = Rehearse.
G = Guard your brain.
E = Enrich your brain.
T = Teach.

#91: Utilize novelty in learning because the brain is attracted to new and fun things; learning happens with novelty.

Novel experiences demand more from the brain and build its ability to compensate. The adaptation-overload principle of exercise applies to the brain and the body. The body and brain adapt to experiences, whether it is strength training with free weights at progressively higher loads or learning to play the piano. The brain and the body grow and get better when a new challenge is presented, which is one of the reasons novelty is a brain booster.

Brain imaging studies show that novel tasks activate larger areas of the brain's cortex. As the task becomes routine and automatic, fewer brain areas are used. Higher levels of the pleasure and reward neurotransmitter dopamine are associated with novelty and creativity. Educational research suggests that novelty increases attention and focus. The take-home message is that people need to do new and different things to engage the brain.

Many simple activities can apply novelty to everyday life, including the following:
- Listen to a different genre of music.
- Try a new food.
- Change your morning routine.
- Read the newspaper beginning and ending with a different section.
- Rearrange the furniture.
- Listen to a new audio book.
- Read a book or magazine that is different from your usual selection.
- Try a new recipe.
- Visit a new location.
- Play a new game.

Special note for teachers: Create novelty in the classroom by altering the learning environment. Eric Jensen, Patricia Wolfe, Laurie Glazener, and Marilee Sprenger are authors with great insights and tips.

#92: Promote quality physical education because exercise helps prepare the brain for optimal learning; children who exercise do better in school.

Quality physical education provides a strong foundation for children to be physically active for life. Quality physical education also positively impacts school performance. Research supports a strong relationship between high academic achievement and high levels of fitness, especially in math and reading. Higher SAT scores are also associated with higher fitness levels.

When schools start to cut programs, physical education, music, and art are often first on the chopping block. It is important to keep quality physical education in schools to improve school performance, support fitness for life, and promote lifelong learning. Studies prove that cutting physical education to allow more time for math, language arts, science, and social sciences does not improve grades or performance on standardized tests. Allowing time for quality physical education with high levels of activity can prepare the brain for optimal learning and improve learning on the following three levels:

- Heightening ability of body systems to function more effectively
- Enhancing the ability of neurons in the brain to connect more efficiently
- Promoting new cell growth

Exercise improves learning by:
- Optimizing the mind-set to improve alertness, attention, and motivation
- Preparing the neurons in the brain to work together to deliver and store information
- Growing new brain cells so the brain can store more information

Students engaged in quality physical education show superior motor fitness, higher academic performance, and a better attitude toward school. Exercise doesn't make a person smarter; it makes a person more ready to learn and remember. Exercise is medicine, and it is important to indoctrinate youth in the importance of physical activity for the body and the brain. Physical education is key to the body and brain health of our nation.

#93: Make connections. Knowledge derives from connections; the essence of memory is linking one thought to another.

Effective teachers and coaches have implemented educator Madeline Hunter's theories for decades. Transfer is one of the most powerful and important principles of learning. Transfer is the ability to make connections between what has been learned and new learning. Transfer occurs when past learning influences the acquisition of new learning. Transfer facilitates creativity, problem solving, and decision-making. Transfer can also shorten the time it takes to acquire new learning.

Similarity, association, degree of original learning, and critical attributes are four factors in learning that can promote making connections in order to transfer learning. One is no more important than the other, and they often operate together to make learning happen.

iStockphoto/Thinkstock

Whenever things have elements that appear similar to the learner, it is more possible that a connection will be made and one learning experience will transfer to another. For example, if a person learns to perform a squat without weights, he is more likely to successfully perform a squat with resistance equipment. If a person learns to use the library to find materials for English class, it is more likely that he will be able to find material in the library for science class.

Whenever feelings or actions occur at the same time, they can be associated, and the presence of one elicits the recall of another. This bonding is especially powerful with feelings associated with concepts or environments. That is why it is so important to provide encouragement and feelings of success in the learning environment.

Information that is well learned will transfer best. If concepts or principles aren't understood, the learner will be unable to connect to more advanced and related concepts. A person who hasn't learned proper alignment for a lunge will not be able to perform lunges in a group exercise class. The degree of original learning is key to making connections.

Critical attributes are the fourth factor to making connections. The identification of the critical attributes that make something what it is helps to solidify understanding. For example, increased respiration and heart rate within the training heart rate zone make an activity aerobic, so swimming, jogging, cycling, and stepping could all be classified as aerobic activities if a person is performing them with the critical attributes of increased respiration and heart rate within the training heart rate zone. Critical attributes are how things are alike and provide a process for identification. The critical attributes of a fruit are that it has seeds inside and it develops from a flower.

Knowledge increases when making connections. Application of the four factors (similarity, association, degree of original learning, and critical attributes) can enhance transfer and the ability to make connections.

#94: Protect your brain.
Guard your brain to avoid injury.

Physical, cognitive, behavioral, or emotional impairments can be caused by brain injury. After brain trauma, persistent cognitive or emotional disabilities can result and may cause difficulty processing information, short-term memory loss, word-finding problems, and inability to focus. There has been a great deal of research and legislation on concussions to protect athletes from negative effects of brain trauma.

Ways to protect the brain include the following:
- Wear a seat belt.
- Wear a helmet for biking, skating, motorcycling, football, and other contact sports.
- Be careful when diving.
- Limit alcohol consumption.
- Don't do drugs.
- Look both ways before crossing the street.

Jupiterimages

#95: Strengthen your senses to engage more of your brain; the brain learns best when more of the five senses are involved.

Strengthening senses can activate new neural pathways in the brain. Information enters the brain through five senses: sight, hearing, smell, taste, and touch. Sight and hearing are used a great deal in daily life. Smell, taste, and touch are sometimes taken for granted.

Some of the strongest memories are associated with smell and taste. Smells of turkey dinner at Thanksgiving or an evergreen tree at Christmas may trigger memories of home. Aromas can also calm and relax the body. Mint is considered a natural brain stimulant. Lavender is a relaxing aroma. Strengthen sense of smell with scented candles or potpourri. Enjoy the scents of nature on a walk in the park, or bring them into the home with live plants and flowers. Using aromatic salts, oils, or bubble bath can add a calming effect to a warm bath.

Taking a bite of food with the nose plugged tastes different than when smell is associated to that bite of food. New neural pathways can develop by exploring new tastes (and smells). Trying new foods surprises the taste buds and the brain.

Looking at what is touched can enhance sense of touch. Touching different fabrics heightens sense of touch. Layering a bed with blankets with a variety of fabrics surrounds the body with soft touch. Massage also heightens sense of touch. Touching and being touched is a human need throughout the lifespan. Pets can serve as companions and also as an opportunity to touch and be touched in a healthy way. Petting a dog or a cat can soothe and calm a person.

#96: Develop spatial abilities to stimulate growth of neurons and dendrites in the part of the brain where spatial abilities reside, typically in the hippocampus and the parietal lobe.

Brain imaging studies have revealed that the area of the brain where spatial abilities reside is more highly developed in cab drivers in large cities. Spatial skills like those involved in putting together puzzles, building with LEGO® bricks, assembling a bicycle, or following a map can be developed and lead to increased achievement in science, technology, engineering, and math.

The hippocampus has place cells that integrate and process special information. The parietal lobe deciphers spatial information and is involved in making sense of where things are in space as well as coordinating necessary motor movement with the cerebellum. Activities that have been found to improve spatial skills include the following:

- Playing video games
- Having musical experiences
- Creating artwork
- Playing LEGO, Lincoln Logs®, Erector® sets
- Participating in sports like basketball, soccer, football, and tennis
- Taking technical education and industrial arts classes

Comstock Images

#97: Play a musical instrument to enhance the ability to process and remember auditory information.

Playing a musical instrument trains the brain to process auditory signals more efficiently and effectively. People who play instruments are better to sort out more important information in a world filled with many sounds and distractions. Playing an instrument helps children to process speech in a noisy classroom. Playing an instrument can help an adult filter out the sounds of the kitchen and competing table talk of others at a restaurant. The more quickly a person can process information, the better that information is remembered. By playing a musical instrument, people are exercising and making important electrical connections and developing neural pathways in the brain. Playing a musical instrument changes the architecture of the brain.

The parts of the brain that control motor skills, process hearing, store audio information, and build memory become larger and more active when a person learns how to play an instrument. Playing a musical instrument improves day-to-day skills such as being alert, planning, and emotional perception. Researchers suggest that learning to play a musical instrument can increase IQ by seven points, in both children and adults.

Playing a musical instrument helps keep the mind alert and active, which plays a role in improving memory skills. Learning to play a musical instrument requires discipline and commitment to practice. The skills learned through practice also provide a sense of accomplishment. It's never too late to start. Playing a musical instrument positively affects the brain at all ages and stages of life.

Brand X Pictures

#98: Believe in yourself. If you think you can or think you can't, you are right.

Self-efficacy is how a person sees his own ability to complete tasks or reach goals. If a person holds the belief that it is within his own power to affect the outcome of situations, he will be more likely to put forth the effort it takes to succeed.

Lifestyle practices that affect health—including exercising, seat belt use, proper diet, dental care, and preventive check-ups—are all choices a person can make for a healthy brain and body. If a person believes in personal power over lifestyle choices like overeating, smoking, or substance abuse, he is more likely to take the steps necessary to improve health habits.

The same is true for achievement in academics, work, and other personal endeavors. Believing the control lies within increases the likelihood of the accomplishment of goals. Those people taking the victim response and believing that things are outside of their control are less likely to put forth the effort necessary to succeed. If you think you can, or think you can't, you are right.

iStockphoto/Thinkstock

#99: Don't smoke. It robs the brain of oxygen.

The brain uses 20 percent of the body's oxygen. Smoking constricts blood flow to the brain. Smoking also increases risk for stroke because chemicals found in cigarette smoke can affect the blood in such a way that it's more prone to clotting. Nicotine damages the interior walls of the blood vessels, increasing risk of atherosclerosis, narrowing of the arteries, making it more difficult for blood to flow efficiently. The body works hard to repair damage caused by cigarette smoke, so stop smoking now for a healthier body. If you don't smoke, don't start.

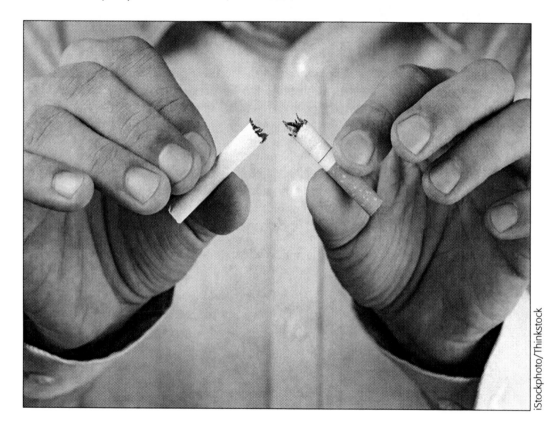

iStockphoto/Thinkstock

#100: Drink alcohol moderately or not at all. Alcohol damages brain cells and interferes with communication between brain cells. Don't do drugs.

Alcohol decreases a person's inhibitions and slows down thought processes because it slows communication to and within the prefrontal cortex, the part of the brain that is responsible for decision-making. When a person is intoxicated, auditory and visual information isn't processed effectively. Connections in the motor area of the brain (cerebellum) are inhibited, causing a person to have trouble with balance, motor control, and speech production. It can take up to 24 hours to metabolize the alcohol in the body, so brain functioning can be impaired for even a day after drinking too much.

Alcohol is especially unsafe for the developing brain. Alcohol affects the hippocampus of the brain, where memories are formed, which is why it is common to forget what has happened when too much alcohol is consumed. Alcohol affects the hypothalamus of the brain, lowering heart rate, respiration, and body temperature.

Heavy drinking over time can negatively affect brain functioning in a variety of ways. Heavy drinking interferes with the ability to plan ahead, increases negative reactions to situations, and decreases the ability to withhold negative responses. Drinking too much inhibits the ability to process and remember information. The ability to decipher spatial information (such as following a map) is damaged as well.

A number of factors influence how and to what extent alcohol affects the brain over time, including the following:
- How much and how often a person drinks
- The age a person started drinking, and how long the person has been drinking
- The person's age, level of education, gender, genetic background, and family history of alcoholism
- Pre-natal alcohol exposure
- A person's body weight, height, and general health

Always eat before consuming alcohol. Drink lots of water before, during, and after drinking. Consider that alcohol abuse damages brain cells and their connections. Alcohol abuse also inhibits the development of new brain cells. Drink moderately or not at all.

#101: Don't just know it; *do it*. What you do with what you know is the key to making a difference in your brain and your life.

It is not what people know; it's what they do with what they know that makes a difference. Awareness and knowledge is the foundation of changing to improve lifestyle or performance. James Prochaska's stages of change can help a person to identify where he is in the process of change.

Pre-contemplation is the first stage of change. During this stage of change, other people may see opportunities for growth or need to change lifestyle to improve health and encourage another person to make changes. During this stage, a person may have no interest in exercising to improve brain and body health, although others are encouraging it.

The second stage of change is contemplation. During this stage a person is thinking about making a change, possibly because of feeling unhealthy and uncomfortable, or maybe because things just aren't working. At this stage, a person may be thinking about exercising or changing eating habits.

Preparation is the stage of change where a person starts to look at options of support for changing lifestyle or behaviors. For example, a person may start to check out fitness centers, personal trainers, and/or nutrition or diet programs. This stage of change is important because choosing an option that works best for that person can mean sticking with it or not. Setting SMART goals are essential at this stage as well. Goals should be *s*pecific, *m*easurable, *a*ttainable, *r*ealistic, and *t*racked regularly.

The action stage of change is when a person begins a new activity or program, or starts to do something different to change behavior and reach a goal. This stage of change is the most exciting as the person is taking charge and making a choice to do new and different things to make life better. This is usually a time when others notice and comment on positive changes the person is making. It is very important that a person takes baby steps and makes small changes in the action stage of change. Doing too much too soon typically results in frustration and decreases chance of success.

The maintenance stage of change occurs when the person is working hard to maintain a new behavior over time. Earlier research suggested that a new habit is formed in an average of 21 days. Current research supports that a new habit or behavior can take anywhere from 18 to 264 days to form, on average approximately 66 days.

It's what you do with what you know that makes a difference in developing lifestyle changes for a healthier brain and body. Don't just know it, *do it.*

References

Adams, T. & Moore, M. et al. (2007). The Relationship Between Physical Activity and Mental Health in a National Sample of College Females. *Women and Health*. 45(1):69–83.

Adlard, P. & Perreau, V. et al. (2005). The Exercise-Induced Expression of BDNF Within the Hippocampus Varies Across Life-span. *Neurobiology of Aging*. 26:511–520.

Almeida, O.P. (2006). Successful Mental Health Aging: Results From a Longitudinal Study of Older Australian Men. *American Journal of Psychiatry*. 14(1):27–35.

Babyak, M. & Blumenthal, J. et al. (2000). Exercise Treatment for Major Depression: Maintenance of Therapeutic Benefit at 10 Months. *Psychosomatic Medicine*. 62:633–638.

Barnes, D. et al. (2003). A Longitudinal Study of Cardiorespiratory Fitness and Cognitive Function in Healthy Older Adults. *American Geriatrics Society*. 51(4):459–465.

Bartholomew, J. & Morrison, D. et al. (2005). Effects of Acute Exercise on Mood and Well-Being in Patients With Major Depressive Disorder. *Medicine and Science in Sports and Exercise*. 37(12):2032–2037.

Berchtold, N.C. et al. (2005). Exercise Primes a Molecular Memory for Brain-Derived Neurotrophic Factor Protein Induction in the Rat Hippocampus. *Neuroscience*. 133:853–861.

Birren, F. (1978). *Color and Human Response*. New York: Van Nostrand Reinhold.

Blaydes-Madigan, J. (2004). *Thinking on Your Feet*. Murphy, Tex.: Action Based Learning.

Blumenthal, J. & Babyak, M. et al. (1999). Effects of Exercise Training on Older Patients With Major Depression. *Archives of Internal Medicine*. 159:2349–2356.

Bonner, A. & Cousins, S. (1996) Exercise and Alzheimer's Disease: Benefits and Barriers. *Activities, Adaptations & Aging*. 20(4):21–24.

Brenes, G. & Williamson, J. et al. (2007). Treatment of Minor Depression in Older Adults: A Pilot Study Comparing Sertraline and Exercise. *Aging and Mental Health*. 11(1):61–68.

Brisswalter, J. & Collardeau, M. et al. (2003). Effects of Acute Physical Exercise Characteristics on Cognitive Performance. *Sports Medicine*. 32(9):555–566.

Broman-Fulks, J. & Berman, M. et al. (2004). Effects of Aerobic Exercise on Anxiety Sensitivity. *Behaviour Research and Therapy*. 42(2):125–136.

Bugg, J. & DeLosh, E. et al. (2006). Physical Activity Moderates Time-of-Day Differences in Older Adults' Working Memory Performance. *Experimental Aging Research*. 32(4):431–446.

Byrne, A. & Byrne, D. (1993). The Effect of Exercise on Depression, Anxiety, and Other Mood States: A Review. *Journal of Psychosomatic Research*. 37(6):565–574.

Caine, et al. (2005). *Brain/Mind Learning Principles in Action*. Thousand Oaks, Calif.: Corwin Press.

Churchill, J. et al. (2002). Exercise, Experience, and the Aging Brain. *Neurobiology of Aging*. 23:941–955.

Coe, D.P. et al. (2006). Effect of Physical Education and Activity Levels on Academic Achievement in Children. *Medicine and Science in Sports and Exercise*. 38(8):1515–1519.

Colcombe, S. & Kramer, A. (2003). Fitness Effects on the Cognitive Function of Older Adults: A Meta-Analytic Study. *American Psychological Society*. 14(2):125–130.

Cooper-Patrick, L. & Ford, D. et al. (1997). Exercise and Depression in Midlife: A Prospective Study. *American Journal of Public Health*. 87(4):670–673.

Cotman, C. & Berchtold, N. (2002). Exercise: A Behavioral Intervention to Enhance Brain Health and Plasticity. *Trends in Neuroscience*. 25(6):295–301.

Cunningham, A. & Stanovich, K. (2001). What Reading Does for the Mind. *Journal of Direct Instruction*. 1(2):137–149.

Dustman, R. & Emmerson, R. et al. (1994). Physical Activity, Age, and Cognitive Neuropsychological Function. *Journal of Aging and Physical Activity*. 2:143–181.

Dustman, R. & Ruhling, R. et al. (1984). Aerobic Exercise Training and Improved Neuropsychological Function of Older Individuals. *Neurobiology of Aging*. 5(1):35–42.

Emery, C. & Gatz, M. (1990). Psychological and Cognitive Effects on an Exercise Program for Community-Residing Older Adults. *The Gerontological Society of America*. 30(2):184–188.

Eriksson, P. & Perfilieva, E. et al. (1998). Neurogenesis in the Adult Human Hippocampus. *Nature Medicine*. 4(11):1313–1317.

Ferris, L.T. et al. (2007). The Effect of Acute Exercise on Serum Brain-Derived Neurotrophic Factor Levels and Cognitive Function. *Medicine and Science in Sport and Exercise*. 39(4)728–734.

Friedland, R. et al. (2001). Patients With Alzheimer's Disease Have Reduced Activities in Midlife Compared With Healthy Control-Group Members. *Proceedings of the National Academy of Sciences of the United States of America*. 98(6):3440–3445.

Gelder, B. et al. (2004). Physical Activity in Relation to Cognitive Decline in Elderly Men: The FINE Study. *Neurology*. 63(12):2316–2321.

Gill, A. & Womack ,R. et al. (2010). Does Exercise Alleviate Symptoms of Depression. *Journal of Family Practice*. 59(9):530–531.

Glazener, L. (2004). *Sensorcises*. San Diego, Calif.: Brain Store.

Greist, J. & Klein, M. et al. (1979). Running as Treatment for Depression. *Comprehensive Psychiatry*. 20(1):41–54.

Grissom, J. (2005). A Study of the Relationship Between Physical Fitness and Academic Achievement in California Using 2004 Test Results. California Physical Fitness Test. California Department of Education.

Hall, C. & Smith, A. et al. (2001). The Impact of Aerobic Activity on Cognitive Function in Older Adults: A New Synthesis Based on the Concept of Executive Control. *European Journal of Cognitive Psychology*. 13(1–2):279–300.

Hannaford, C. (1995). *Smart Moves*. Arlington, Va.: Great Ocean Publishing.

Howard, P. (2006). *The Owner's Manual for the Brain*. Austin, Tex.: Bard Press.

Hunter, R. (2004). *Madeline Hunter's Mastery Teaching*. Thousand Oaks, Calif.: Corwin Press.

Jensen, E. (2008). *Learning With the Body in Mind*. Thousand Oaks, Calif.: Corwin Press.

Jensen, E. (1998). *Teaching With the Brain in Mind*. Alexandria, Va.: Association for Supervision and Curriculum Development.

Kramer, A. & Colcombe, S. et al. (2005). Fitness, Aging and Neurocognitive Function. *Neurobiology of Aging*. 26S:124–127.

Lachman, M.E. et al. (2006). The Effects of Strength Training on Memory in Older Adults. *Journal of Aging and Physical Activity*. 14(1):59–73.

Larson, E. et al. (2006). Exercise Is Associated With Reduced Risk for Incident Dementia among Persons 65 Years of Age and Older. *Annals of Internal Medicine*. 144(2):73–82.

Larun, L. & Nordheim, L. et al. (2006). Exercise in Prevention and Treatment of Anxiety and Depression Among Children and Young People. Cochrane Database of Systematic Reviews. 3.

Laurin, D. & Verreault, R. et al. (2001). Physical Activity and Risk of Cognitive Impairment and Dementia in Elderly Persons. *Archives of Neurology*. 58(3):498.

Lawlor, D. & Hopker, S. (2001). The Effectiveness of Exercise as an Intervention in the Management of Depression: Systemic Review and Meta-Regression Analysis of Randomized Controlled Trials. *BMJ*. 322(1):1–8.

Ledoux, J. & Gorman, J. (2001). A Call to Action: Overcoming Anxiety Through Active Coping. *American Journal of Psychiatry*. 158(12):1953–1955.

Lee, A. & Ogle, W. et al. (2002). Stress and Depression: Possible Links to Neuron Death in the Hippocampus. *Bipolar Disorders*. 4:117–128.

Martinsen, E. & Hoffart, A. et al. (2000). Aerobic and Non-Aerobic Forms of Exercise in the Treatment of Anxiety Disorders. *Stress Medicine*. 5(2):115–120.

Medina, J. (2008). *Brain Rules*. Seattle, Wash.: Pear Press.

Medved, D. (2011). *Ageless Grace*. Hendersonville, N.C.: Purple Iris Press.

Moore, K. & Blumenthal, J. (1998). Exercise Training as an Alternative Treatment for Depression Among Older Adults. *Alternative Therapies in Health and Medicine*. 4(1):48–56.

Moul, J. & Goldman, B. et al. (1995). Physical Activity and Cognitive Performance in the Older Population. *Journal of Aging and Physical Activity*. 3:135–145.

Neeper, S. et al. (1995). Exercise and Brain Neurotrophins. *Nature*. 373:109.

Oeland, A. & Laessoe, U. et al. (2010). Impact of Exercise on Patients With Depression and Anxiety. *Nordic Journal of Psychiatry*. 64:210–217.

Ogle, L. & Sapolsky, R. (2002). Stress and Depression: Possible Links to Neuron Death in the Hippocampus. *Bipolar Disorders*. 4(2):117–128.

Otto, M. & Church, T. et al. (2007). Exercise for Mood and Anxiety Disorders. *The Journal of Clinical Psychiatry*. 9(4):287–294.

Peck, H. & Kehle, T. et al. (2005). Yoga as an Intervention for Children With Attention Problems. *School Psychology Review*. 34(3):415–424.

Petrovitch, H. & White, L. (2005). Exercise and Cognitive Function. *The Lancet Neurology*. 4(11):690–691.

Prochaska, J. (1994). *Changing for Good*. New York: Avon Books.

Ratey, J. (2008). SPARK: *The Revolutionary New Science of Exercise and the Brain*. New York: Little Brown and Company.

Russo-Neustadt, A. & Beard, R. et al. (1999). Exercise, Antidepressant Medications, and Enhanced Brain Derived Neurotrophic Factor Expression. *Neuropsychopharmacology*. 21(5):680–682.

Sallis, J. et al. (1999). Effects of Health-Related Physical Education on Academic Achievement: Project SPARK. *Research Quarterly for Exercise and Sport*. 70(2):127–134.

Salmon, P. (2001). Effects of Physical Exercise on Anxiety, Depression, and Sensitivity to Stress: A Unifying Theory. *Clinical Psychology Review*. 2(1):33–61.

Schunk, D. (2012). *Learning Theories*. Boston, Mass.: Pearson.

Scully, D. & Kremer, J. et al. (1998). Physical Exercise and Psychological Well Being: A Critical Review. *British Journal of Sports Medicine*. 32:111–120.

Sibley, B. & Etnier, J. (2003). The Relationship Between Physical Activity and Cognition in Children: A Meta-Analysis. *Pediatric Exercise Science*. 15:243–256.

Sousa, D. (2001). *How the Brain Learns*. Thousand Oaks, Calif.: Corwin Press

Sprenger, M. (2007). *Memory 101 for Educators*. Thousand Oaks, Calif.: Corwin Press.

Summerford, C. (2009). *Action-Packed Classroom: K–5*. Thousand Oaks, Calif.: Corwin Press.

Sweeney, M. (2009). *Brain: The Complete Mind*. Washington, D.C.: National Geographic.

Szabo, A. (2003). The Acute Effects of Humor and Exercise on Mood and Anxiety. *Journal of Leisure Research*. 35(2):152–162.

Tsang, H. & Fung, K. et al. (2006). Effect of a Qigong Exercise Program on Elderly With Depression. *International Journal of Geriatric Psychiatry.* 21:890–897.

Verghese, J. & Lipton, R. et al. (2003). Leisure Activities and the Risk of Dementia in the Elderly. *The New England Journal of Medicine.* 348(25):2508–2516.

Welk, G. & Joens-Matre, R. (2007). The Effects of Weight on Self-Concept, and Psychosocial Correlates of Physical Activity in Youths. *Journal of Physical Education, Recreation, and Dance.* 78(8):43–46.

Weuve, J. et al. (2004). Physical Activity, Including Walking, and Cognitive Function in Older Women. *The Journal of the American Medical Association.* 292(12):1454–1461.

Winningham, R. (2010). *Train Your Brain: How to Maximize Memory Ability in Older Adulthood.* Amityville, N.Y.: Baywood Publishing Company.

Winter, B. et al. (2007). High Impact Running Improves Learning. *Neurobiology of Learning and Memory.* 87(4):597–609.

Wolfe, P. (2001). *Brain Matters.* Alexandria, Va.: Association for Supervision and Curriculum Development.

About the Author

Terry Eckmann, Ph.D. is a professor at Minot State University. Eckmann has over 30 years experience in the fitness industry. She presents internationally on topics related to health and fitness. She has written articles for *IDEA Fitness Journal*, ICAA's *Journal on Active Aging*, *Club Success*, and *Fitness Management*. Eckmann authored the pedagogy chapter for the *ACSM Personal Training Manual* and the customer service chapter for Human Kinetics' *Health Fitness Management* (2nd edition). She serves on the advisory board of the International Council on Active Aging. Eckmann hosts KXMC-TV's "Eye on Fitness," a fitness segment on the noon show for the Minot viewing region. Eckmann received the NDAHPERD Honor Award in 2010, the NDAHERD University Teacher of the Year Award in 2007, and the Minot State University Faculty Achievement Award for Research and Scholarship in 2007. Eckmann received the North Dakota Picture of Health Award in 2003 and the Toastmaster's Excellence in Communication and Leadership Award in 2002. Eckmann has also been nationally recognized for her work in the fitness industry. She received the IDEA Make Fitness Happen award in 1996 and the 1997 Club Industry Distinguished Business Award for Industry Enhancement. Eckmann worked as a speech-language pathologist prior to beginning full-time work in the fitness industry. *101 Brain Boosters* combines Eckmann's expertise as a researcher, educator, fitness professional, and speech-language pathologist to create a book that combines brain-based research with practical tips for anyone interested in living a brain-healthy lifestyle.